SENSATIONAL 70s QUIZ BOOK

SENSATIONAL

70s

QUIZ

BOOK

BRIAN WILLIAMS

Miles Kelly
PUBLISHING

First published in 2000 by
Miles Kelly Publishing Ltd
Bardfield Centre
Great Bardfield
Essex CM7 4SL

2468109753

ISBN 1 90294 724 X

Editor Clive Gifford
Editorial Assistant Mark Darling
Cover Design Jo Brewer
Design Management Jo Brewer
Page Layout Helen Weller
Production Rachel Jones

INTRODUCTION

When we look at a movie or TV programme from the 70s doesn't it all seem nearly normal, but not quite? The clothes do not enjoy the paisleys and swirls of the 60s, but they have daring and vibrant colours compared with the more sober hues of today. Many of the cars are still on our roads and many of us have photograph albums full of pictures showing strange-looking cousins from distant lands – ourselves!

We saw movies like *The Godfather*, *A Bridge Too Far*, *Midnight Cowboy*, *Rollerball* and *MASH*, but can we remember who directed them and starred in them? Just three decades ago, but those names from politics and the arts: Iain Macleod, Malcom Fraser, John Stonehouse and William Styron – they have a tantalizing echo, but who exactly were they? What exactly were they famous for? Mark Spitz, Joe Bugner, Shane Gould, Roger Millward – all household names in the sporting world of the 70s. Not quite so household now.

These quizzes will bring it all back – if it was ever there to begin with. And if it wasn't, it soon will be!

QUIZ 1
POT LUCK

🍀🍀🍀🍀🍀🍀🍀🍀🍀🍀🍀🍀🍀🍀🍀🍀🍀🍀🍀🍀🍀🍀🍀🍀🍀🍀🍀🍀🍀🍀🍀🍀

1 Who recorded a 1976 album called *Children of the World*?

2 Which long running soap opera screened its 1000th episode in August, 1970?

3 By what method was convicted double murderer Gary Gilmore executed?

4 *Up Around the Bend* was a 1970 hit for which group?

5 Mother Teresa, the Nobel Peace Prize winner of 1979, was born in which country?

6 Which band followed *Figaro* in 1978 with a song called *Beautiful Lover*?

7 The first woman to climb Mount Everest, Junko Tabei, was from which country?

8 Which Hollywood legend was paid $2 million for his cameo appearance in *Superman*?

9 What did Michael Angelow do at Lord's, setting a precedent?

10 After a run of bad results in 1975 the Soviet national football team were replaced by which club side?

11 Which country abolished the death penalty in July, 1976?

12 What was the first ever arcade video game, which was released in 1978?

13 Louise Brown, the world's first 'test-tube baby' was born in which English town?

14 Which former US President died in January, 1973?

15 Who won the Wimbledon men's title in the centenary year of 1977?

🍀🍀🍀🍀🍀🍀🍀🍀🍀🍀🍀🍀🍀🍀🍀🍀🍀🍀🍀🍀🍀🍀🍀🍀🍀🍀🍀🍀🍀🍀🍀🍀

ANSWERS

1. The Bee Gees 2. *Coronation Street* 3. He was shot by a five-man firing squad 4. Creedence Clearwater Revival 5. Albania (now Macedonia) 6. Brotherhood of Man 7. Japan 8. Marlon Brando 9. He was the first streaker at a Test match in England 10. Dynamo Kiev 11. Canada 12. Space Invaders 13. Oldham 14. Lyndon B Johnson 15. Bjorn Borg

QUIZ 2
ARTS &
ENTERTAINMENT

1 Which hotel gave its name to a comedy series on British television?

2 Who starred as the hotel's manic owner?

3 What was the name of his wife, played by Prunella Scales?

4 Eric and Ernie were Britain's top comedians in the 70s. What were their full names?

5 Which Benny was a comic hit on both sides of the Atlantic?

6 Who tittered his way *Up Pompeii*?

7 With which film series, starting in the 70s, is George Lucas most famously linked?

8 What was the name of the frog in *The Muppet Show*?

9 By whom was he constantly and amorously pursued?

10 *Plunder* by Ben Travers was the first production at which new London theatre in 1976?

11 Which ship featured in a 1978 BBC television documentary with the theme tune *Sailing*?

12 Who had a hit with his version of the song?

13 Who played Hercule Poirot in the 1977 film of *Death on the Nile*?

14 Which art forger owned up to painting Palmers and Constables?

15 What did Angela Rippon and Kenneth Kendall do at night on BBC TV?

ANSWERS

1. *Fawlty Towers* 2. John Cleese 3. Sybil 4. Eric Morecambe and Ernie Wise 5. Benny Hill 6. Frankie Howerd 7. *Star Wars* 8. Kermit 9. Miss Piggy 10. The National Theatre 11. The aircraft carrier HMS *Ark Royal* 12. Rod Stewart 13. Peter Ustinov 14. Tom Keating 15. Read the news

QUIZ 3
PEOPLE

ꞏꞏꞏꞏꞏꞏꞏꞏꞏꞏꞏꞏꞏꞏꞏꞏꞏꞏꞏꞏꞏꞏꞏꞏꞏꞏꞏꞏꞏꞏꞏꞏꞏꞏꞏꞏꞏꞏꞏ

1 Who succeeded Harold Wilson in 1976 as prime minister of the United Kingdom?

2 Which president of Cyprus was forced into exile in 1974?

3 In 1971 Lord Robens resigned in protest from the chairmanship of which body?

4 Prince Souphanouvong became president in 1975 of which country?

5 Who was secretary of state for industry in Harold Wilson's 1974 government?

6 From which African people did Chief Buthelezi come?

7 To which prime minister was Lady Falkender an adviser?

8 Which U.S. president resigned in 1974?

9 Who played Prospero on his 70th birthday, in Peter Hall's production of *The Tempest*?

10 What voyage did Kenichi Horie complete in 1974?

11 Which former prime minister of Greece was exiled to an island in 1974?

12 Who was president of France in 1970?

13 What type of vehicle did Evel Knievel use for his stunts?

14 Who played Rose in the television series *Upstairs, Downstairs*?

15 Which country did Colonel Mengistu dominate in 1977?

ꞏꞏꞏꞏꞏꞏꞏꞏꞏꞏꞏꞏꞏꞏꞏꞏꞏꞏꞏꞏꞏꞏꞏꞏꞏꞏꞏꞏꞏꞏꞏꞏꞏꞏꞏꞏꞏꞏꞏ
ANSWERS

1, James Callaghan 2, Archbishop Makarios 3, The National Coal Board 4, Laos 5, Anthony Wedgwood Benn 6, Zulus 7, Harold Wilson 8, Richard Nixon 9, Sir John Gielgud 10, The first solo nonstop circumnavigation under sail 11, Georgios Papadopoulos 12, Georges Pompidou 13, A motorcycle 14, Jean Marsh 15, Ethiopia

POT LUCK

•••

1 What was Alan Hudson's sport?

2 Who was the first boxer to beat Muhammad Ali in a world title fight?

3 Which forms did people in the UK love to fill in in 1971?

4 What was withdrawn from schools in 1971?

5 Who wrote *The Exorcist*?

6 Who played the film role of a girl possessed by the Devil?

7 Who said he'd tax the rich until the pips squeak?

8 Who opened Sydney's opera home in 1973?

9 Where did Rauf Denktash lead a separatist movement?

10 What art did Dame Barbara Hepworth practice?

11 Which US horse race celebrated its centenary in 1975?

12 In which country did FRELIMO operate?

13 Which British crime writer died in 1976?

14 Who was called a 'Cold War Witch'?

15 And by whom?

•••

ANSWERS

1 Soccer 2. Joe Frazier 3. Census forms 4. Free milk 5. William Blatty 6. Linda Blair 7. Denis Healey 8. The Queen 9. Turkish part of Cyprus 10. Sculpture 11. The Kentucky Derby 12. Mozambique 13. Agatha Christie 14. Margaret Thatcher 15. Pravda, The Soviet Union

QUIZ 5
SCIENCE & TECHNOLOGY

●●

1 Which country played the leading part in developing the *Ariane* rocket?

2 In which year did Concorde begin regular flights to and from Washington?

3 In what kind of work did Red Adair specialize in the 70s?

4 In 1974 *Pioneer 11* passed by Jupiter and headed for which planet?

5 Which great dam in Egypt began operating in 1971?

6 Which country chilled a lava flow with seawater to prevent a harbour being blocked?

7 What was Norpax?

8 The title of the 1974 film *Day for Night* referred to which cinematic technique?

9 What award did Sir Martin Ryle share with Antony Hewish in 1974?

10 Quasi-stellar radio sources were investigated in the 70s. What is the short name for them?

11 Which country played the largest part in helping Egypt to build the Aswan High Dam?

12 Kitty Hawk was one of the modules of the *Apollo 14* spacecraft. Which module?

13 The flight of *Soyuz 11* set a new endurance record in 1971. How did it end?

14 Which Nobel prize winner claimed that vitamin C can treat or prevent the common cold?

15 After whom were MiG aircraft named?

●●

ANSWERS

1. France 2. 1976 3. Dealing with oil-well fires and blow-outs 4. Saturn 5. The Aswan High Dam 6. Iceland 7. The North Pacific Experiment, a study of ocean currents and climate 8. Shooting a night scene in daylight 9. The Nobel prize for physics 10. Quasars 11. The Soviet Union 12. The command module 13. The cosmonauts died during re-entry 14. Linus Pauling 15. Their designers Mikoyan and Gurevich

ARTS &
ENTERTAINMENT

1 In which film of a D H Lawrence novel did Glenda Jackson and Jennie Linden co-star?

2 What animal featured in the film *Kes*?

3 What was the setting for the television comedy series *Porridge*?

4 Who was the star, as Fletcher?

5 A young actor appeared in *Porridge*, *Rising Damp* and other comedies of the decade; he died in 1979. Who was he?

6 *Murder on the Orient Express* was filmed in 1974; who played the detective Hercule Poirot?

7 Who wrote the original book of *Murder on the Orient Express*?

8 Who wrote the play *Sleuth*?

9 A stolen picture called *The Guitar Player* was found in London in 1974; who painted it: Van Gogh, Vermeer or Rembrandt?

10 What was the title of the BBC television series set in a German castle during World War II?

11 What was the title of Alexander Solzhenitsyn's book about the Soviet slave labour camps?

12 Which fish spashed onto the scene in a book by Peter Benchley?

13 Complete the title of this 1977 movie … *Close Encounters of*?

14 Who wrote the music for the animated film of *Watership Down*?

15 Where did the TV character Uncle Bulgaria live?

ANSWERS

1. *Women in Love* (1970) 2. A kestrel 3. A prison 4. Ronnie Barker 5. Richard Beckinsale 6. Albert Finney 7. Agatha Christie 8. Anthony Shaffer 9. Vermeer 10. *Colditz* 11. *The Gulag Archipelago* 12. *Jaws* 13. *The Third kind* 14. Art Garfunkel 15. Wimbledon Common (he was one of the *Wombles*)

WORLD EVENTS

1 What name was given in the 70s to Britain's dispute with Iceland over fishing limits?

2 In which year did the Nigerian civil war end with the defeat of Biafra?

3 What do the initials OAS stand for in international affairs?

4 At which airport were 26 people killed in a terrorist attack in 1972?

5 In which year was Ceylon renamed Sri Lanka?

6 In which country did the military junta resign, during a crisis in relations with Turkey?

7 What did the 26th Amendment to the U.S. Constitution do?

8 What centenary was celebrated in the Soviet Union in April 1970?

9 In which country is the Plaine des Jarres?

10 Which countries formed the short-lived Confederation of Arab Republics?

11 Which empire purported to celebrate its 2500th anniversary in 1971?

12 GATT ended its 26th general assembly in Geneva in 1970. What is GATT?

13 The Pentagon papers were published in 1971. What were they about?

14 Which London thoroughfare was the scene of a kidnapping attempt on Princess Anne?

15 Which European Communist state opposed the Soviet Union and supported China?

ANSWERS

1, The cod wars 2, 1970 3, Organization of American States 4, Tel Aviv 5, 1972 6, Greece 7, It extended full voting rights to 18-year-olds 8, The birth of Lenin 9, Laos 10, Egypt, Libya and Syria 11, Persia (Iran) 12, General Agreement on Tariffs and Trade 13, U.S. involvement in Vietnam 14, The Mall 15, Albania

QUIZ 8
SPORT

•••

1 In 1978, who became the first man ever to win the world heavyweight boxing title for the third time?

2 Which princess was Britain's sportswoman of the year in 1971?

3 What sport was she prominent in?

4 Which politician sailed to victory in the 1971 Admiral's Cup yacht race?

5 Which diminutive gymnast was a star of the 1972 Munich Olympics?

6 Which American swimmer won seven gold medals at the 1972 Olympics?

7 Which team won cricket's first World Cup, in 1975?

8 In which sport was Ivan Mauger of New Zealand a 70s star?

9 What was Jonah Barrington's sport?

10 Who became the first British rider to win the world showjumping title in 1970?

11 Where were the 9th Comonwealth Games held in 1970?

12 Which country won the 1970 soccer World Cup?

13 Who played in the longest-ever Wimbledon women's singles final, in 1970?

14 Which player won?

15 Which racehorse dominated European racetracks in 1970?

•••

ANSWERS

1, Muhammad Ali 2, Princess Anne 3, Three-day event horse riding 4, Edward Heath 5, Olga Korbut 6, Mark Spitz 7, West Indies 8, Speedway 9, Squash 10, David Broome 11, Edinburgh 12, Brazil 13, Margaret Court and Billie-Jean King 14, Margaret Court 15, Nijinsky

QUIZ 9
ARTS &
ENTERTAINMENT

1 In which TV show did Penelope Keith play Margot ?

2 Who played her husband?

3 Who collaborated to bring the world *Jesus Christ Superstar*?

4 *Time and Time Again* was one of many hit plays by ... who?

5 Who starred in the first production of Godspell and went on to success as a solo artiste?

6 Who wrote the play *Jumpers*?

7 Which ex-*Avengers* actress starred in the London production?

8 Whose 1971 production of *A Midsummer Night's Dream* became legendary?

9 Which former model appeared in a 1971 film of *The Boyfriend*?

10 Who directed the film?

11 Which puppet appeared with Harry Corbett?

12 Who was the puppet's doggy friend?

13 Who played Captain Mainwaring on TV?

14 In which show?

15 What job did Corporal Jones do in this show?

ANSWERS

1. *The Good Life* 2, Paul Eddington 3, Tim Rice and Andrew Lloyd-Webber 4, Alan Ayckbourne 5, David Essex 6, Tom Stoppard 7, Diana Rigg 8, Peter Brook 9, Twiggy 10, Ken Russell 11, Sooty 12, Sweep 13, Arthur Lowe 14, *Dad's Army* 15, He was the local butcher

QUIZ 10
POT LUCK

●●

1   Who sang *Bright Eyes* in 1979?

2   What animals featured in the film from which it came?

3   What was the film's title?

4   Which schoolteacher became the focus of anti-police protests after his death at a rally?

5   Which country did an Israeli premier visit for the first time in 1979?

6   Of which country, did Bishop Muzorewa became prime minister in 1979?

7   Where do passengers ride the Jubilee Line?

8   In which TV show did Maureen Lipman play an agony aunt?

9   What was Kelly Monteith's native country?

10 Was he a singer, a comedian or a weatherman?

11 Who played George Cole's minder?

12 Which party won the UK's 1979 general election?

13 Who then became prime minister?

14 Who became chancellor of the exchequer?

15 Which famous boxer quit the ring in 1979?

●●

ANSWERS

1, Art Garfunkel 2, Rabbits 3, *Watership Down* 4, Blair Peach 5, Egypt 6, Rhodesia 7, London 8, Agony 9, Canada 10, A comedian 11, Dennis Waterman 12, The Conservatives 13, Margaret Thatcher 14, Geoffrey Howe 15, Muhammad Ali

QUIZ 11
WORLD EVENTS

1 ELF was active in East Africa in the 70s. What do the initials stand for?

2 The United States bicentennial was in 1976. Exactly what happened on 4 July 1776?

3 Mozambique became independent in 1975. Which country ruled it before that?

4 Which country was known as the United Arab Republic in the early 70s?

5 Who became dictator of Uganda in 1971?

6 In which year in the 70s was local government in England and Wales reformed?

7 What was the name of ITV's main arts programme in the mid-70s?

8 Diego Garcia was leased to the U.S. as a base in 1975. Where is it?

9 Which year in the mid-70s did the Pope declare a Holy Year?

10 What did the Annan Committee of the 70s consider?

11 Was the comedy series *The Goodies* broadcast by the BBC or by ITV?

12 Abu Musa was seized by Iran in 1971. Who or what is Abu Musa?

13 Why did the U.S. and South Vietnam invade Cambodia in 1970?

14 What new name did the Ellice Islands adopt in 1975?

15 Which pan-African meeting did Idi Amin chair in 1975?

ANSWERS

1, Eritrean Liberation Front 2, Congress adopted the Declaration of Independence 3, Portugal 4, Egypt 5, Idi Amin 6, 1974 7, *Aquarius* 8, In the Indian Ocean 9, 1975 10, The future of broadcasting in the United Kingdom 11, The BBC 12, An island in the Persian Gulf 13, To cut North Vietnam's supply lines to the south 14, Tuvalu 15, Organization of African Unity summit conference at Kampala

QUIZ 12
PEOPLE

●●

1 Who represented Israel at Camp David in 1978?

2 Who received a 'full, free and absolute pardon' in 1974?

3 Who starred in the film of *The Great Gatsby*?

4 In which country was Mordecai Richler born?

5 Of which country did Fakhruddin Ali Ahmed become president in 1974?

6 With which form of handcraft did Erica Wilson make her name?

7 Which award did Sean MacBride share with Eisaku Sato in 1974?

8 What post did Clifford Dupont take up in 1970?

9 Who directed the 1971 film *A Clockwork Orange*?

10 Who wrote *Master and Commander*?

11 The poet Pablo Neruda won the 1971 Nobel prize for literature. What was his nationality?

12 Who became Malawi's "president for life" in 1971?

13 Louis Armstrong died in 1971. By what nickname was he known?

14 By what name has Karol Wojtyla been known since 1978?

15 William O Douglas resigned in 1975. What position had he held for 36 years?

●●

ANSWERS

1, Menachem Begin 2, Richard Nixon 3, Robert Redford 4, Canada 5, India 6, Embroidery or needlecraft 7, The Nobel prize for peace 8, President of the self-styled Rhodesian Republic 9, Stanley Kubrick 10, Patrick O'Brien 11, Chilean 12, Hastings Banda 13, Satchmo 14, Pope John Paul II 15, Justice of the U.S. Supreme Court

QUIZ 19
SPORT

●●●

1 In which 1970 race did Intrepid beat Gretel?

2 For whom did Rohan Kanhai play international Test cricket?

3 What did Blue Flame do faster than anything before?

4 Was its driver: a) Gary Gabelich or b) Donald Campbell?

5 Was Ken Buchanan a '70s champion boxer, motorcycle racer, or swimmer?

6 British athletics had a new London home in 1971 for major championships. Where?

7 In which sport did David Wilkie of Great Britain set a world record in 1973?

8 Who won the 1973 men's singles at Wimbledon?

9 Which world boxing title did John Conteh win in 1974?

10 Whom did West Germany beat 3-2 in the 1970 soccer World Cup semi final?

11 Which soccer star was accused of stealing jewellery in 1970 during a pre-World Cup tour?

12 Who was the manager of the England team for the 1970 World Cup?

13 Which country did Ian Chappell captain at cricket in the 70s?

14 What year did Arthur Ashe win Wimbledon?

15 In which sport did John Curry win Olympic gold?

●●●

ANSWERS

1, America's Cup (for yachts) 2, West Indies 3, Travelled on land (new land speed record holder) 4, a) 5, Boxer 6, Crystal Palace 7, Swimming (200 m breaststroke) 8, Jan Kodes 9, Light heavyweight 10, England 11, Bobby Moore 12, Sir Alf Ramsey 13, Australia 14, 1975 15, Figure skating

QUIZ 14
WORLD EVENTS

1 Which country was taken over by the Khmer Rouge in the early 70s?

2 In 1976 Nigeria announced plans for a new capital. What is it called?

3 What happened at Kent State University in 1970?

4 In which year did Britain vote in a referendum to remain in the EEC?

5 In 1975 a buffer zone between Egyptian and Israeli forces was agreed. Where was it?

6 Who was elected president of Chile in 1970?

7 To which country was the crown of St. Stephen returned in 1978?

8 What made ITV stop broadcasting for three months in 1979?

9 Who were "Nader's raiders"?

10 What title did Mohammed Reza Pahlavi hold before his overthrow?

11 Which country invaded Uganda in 1979?

12 Which Benjamin Britten opera was commissioned by BBC2?

13 What word was coined for the combination of inflation and industrial stagnation?

14 Which emperor was dethroned in 1974?

15 In 1972 the liner Queen Elizabeth was destroyed by fire. Where?

ANSWERS

1. Cambodia 2. Abuja 3. Four students were shot dead by the National Guard 4. 1975 5. In Sinai, east of the Suez Canal 6. Salvador Allende 7. Hungary 8. A strike over pay 9. Consumerist followers of Ralph Nader in the U.S. 10. Shah-in-shah or emperor of Iran 11. Tanzania 12. Owen Wingrave 13. Stagflation 14. Emperor Haile Selassie of Ethiopia 15. In Hong Kong Harbour

QUIZ 15
ARTS &
ENTERTAINMENT

●●●

1 Who wrote *The Far Pavilions* (1978)?

2 Who wrote *In the Shadow of Man*?

3 Which animals was this book about: dogs, apes or horses?

4 Who was the author of the novel *Jake's Thing*?

5 Which book by Tim Severin described an Atlantic voyage recreating the journey of a medieval Irish monk?

6 Which book was the religious bestseller of 1970?

7 Cornelius Ryan's 1974 book about Arnhem was called … what?

8 Saul Bellow won the 1976 Nobel Prize for literature; was he best known for poems, plays or novels?

9 Which American wrote a 1977 book about his African origins?

10 Which actor wrote a memoir called *A Postillion Struck by Lightning*?

11 A diary by Edith Holden became a 70s bestseller; what was it full title?

12 *Sunset at Blandings* was the last book from which comic writer?

13 Who was the writer of *Some of Me Poetry* (1976)?

14 Which Henry made a rare appearance on the London stage in 1975?

15 Who wrote the play *No Man's Land*?

●●●

ANSWERS

1, M M Kaye 2, Jane Goodall 3, Apes 4, Kingsley Amis 5, *The Brendan Voyage* 6, *The New English Bible* 7, *A Bridge Too Far* 8, Novels 9, Alex Haley 10, Dirk Bogarde 11, *The Country Diary of an Edwardian Lady* 12, P G Wodehouse 13, Pam Ayres 14, Henry Fonda 15, Harold Pinter

QUIZ 16
PEOPLE

●●●

1 Who wrote *The Memoirs of a Survivor*, published in 1975?

2 What post did Bruno Kreisky take up in 1970?

3 Park Chung Hee was assassinated in 1979. Of which country was he president?

4 Who directed *Last Tango in Paris*?

5 Of which country was Abba Eban foreign minister?

6 In a referendum in Liechtenstein in 1971, what electoral proposal was defeated?

7 Who directed the 1972 film *The Godfather*?

8 In which country was Patricio Aylwin leader of the Christian Democrats in the mid-70s?

9 Houari BoumÈdienne died in 1978. Of which country was he president?

10 Which emperor visited China in 1971 and was greeted by Chairman Mao?

11 Who wrote *Humboldt's Gift*?

12 What was the nationality of U.N. secretary-general U Thant?

13 Alan Shepard was America's first man in space. Did he ever reach the Moon?

14 Of which country was Juan Maria Bordaberry elected president?

15 Francois Duvalier died in 1971. Which country had he ruled for 14 years?

●●●

ANSWERS

1, Doris Lessing 2, Chancellor of Austria 3, Korea 4, Bernardo Bertolucci 5, Israel 6, The granting of voting rights to women 7, Francis Ford Coppola 8, Chile 9, Algeria 10, Haile Selassie of Ethiopia 11, Saul Bellow 12, Burmese 13, Yes, in Apollo 14 14, Uruguay 15, Haiti

QUIZ 17
POT LUCK

●●

1   What did Snow Knight win in 1974?

2   What happened at Flixborough that year?

3   What was Tony Greig's sport?

4   What post did Jacques Chirac take up in 1974?

5   Who was Donald Coggan?

6   Which lord disappeared from home in 1974?

7   With which London gambling club was he linked?

8   What was this lord's nickname?

9   Of what crime was he suspected?

10 Who played Roy Neary in a film about aliens?

11 And what was the film?

12 Who played 007 in *The Spy Who Loved me*?

13 Who won the FA Cup in 1977?

14 Which song took the Eagles to the top of the charts that year?

15 Where did the Royal Navy pull out its last warship from in 1979?

●●

ANSWERS

1, The Derby 2, A chemical plant explosion killed 29 people 3, Cricket 4, French premier 5, Archbishop of Canterbury (1974) 6, Lord Lucan 7, The Clermont 8, Lucky 9, Murdering the family nanny (in mistake for his wife) 10, Richard Dreyfuss 11, *Close Encounters of the Third Kind* 12, Roger More 13, Manchester United 14, *Hotel California* 15, Malta

QUIZ 18
SPORT

🐌🐌🐌🐌🐌🐌🐌🐌🐌🐌🐌🐌🐌🐌🐌🐌🐌🐌🐌🐌🐌🐌🐌🐌🐌🐌🐌🐌🐌🐌🐌🐌🐌🐌🐌

1 In which sport was Viv Richards a dominant force?

2 What year did Southampton win the FA Cup?

3 In which sport was Geoff Hunt a champion?

4 And in which sport did James Hunt make his name?

5 Which team beat Arsenal to win the 1978 FA Cup final?

6 Where were the 1978 Commonwealth Games staged?

7 In which event did Britain reach the final in 1978, for the first time in 41 years?

8 Two brothers were in the team; who were they?

9 Did Britain win?

10 What adventure did Naomi James complete on 8 June 1978?

11 Who rode Empery to win the 1975 English Derby?

12 Which Scottish sporting body celebrated its centenary in 1973?

13 Who captained Scotland into the 1974 World Cup soccer finals?

14 Which club side he play for?

15 Which race's distance was changed from 525 yards to 500 metres (547 yards) in 1975?

🐌🐌🐌🐌🐌🐌🐌🐌🐌🐌🐌🐌🐌🐌🐌🐌🐌🐌🐌🐌🐌🐌🐌🐌🐌🐌🐌🐌🐌🐌🐌🐌🐌🐌🐌
ANSWERS

1, Cricket 2, 1976 3, Squash 4, Motor racing 5, Ipswich Town 6, Edmonton, Canada 7, The Davis Cup (tennis) 8, John and David Lloyd 9, No, they were beaten by the United States 10, A round-the-world voyage 11, Lester Piggott 12, Scottish Football Association 13, Billy Bremner 14, Leeds United 15, The Greyhound Derby

QUIZ 19
WORLD EVENTS

🖤🖤🖤

1 In which year did the United Natioons admit the People's Republic of China?

2 What nickname was given to Britainís National Economic Development Council?

3 In the second election of 1974, which party gained 30% of the Scottish vote?

4 In which year did direct rule in Northern Ireland begin?

5 Jigme Singye Wangchuk became king of which country in 1972?

6 Which fruit and vegetable market replaced Covent Garden in London?

7 By what name was Namibia formerly known?

8 Which organization was expelled from Jordan in 1971?

9 Which emperor was overthrown in 1979?

10 What extremist Palestinian terrorist group was formed in 1971?

11 What was the Lomé Convention of 1975?

12 Which civil war took place on the Indian subcontinent in 1971?

13 What did the "White House tapes" record?

14 Which U.S. president visited China in 1972?

15 In 1976 the president of Argentina was overthrown. What was her surname?

🖤🖤🖤

ANSWERS

1, 1971 2, 'Neddy' 3, SNP, the Scottish National Party 4, 1972 5, Bhutan 6, Nine Elms 7, South West Africa 8, The Palestine Liberation Organization 9, Emperor Bokassa of Central Africa 10, 'Black September' 11, Agreement between the EEC and 46 African, Caribbean and Pacific countries 12, Civil war between East and West Pakistan 13, President Nixon's conversations 14, Richard Nixon 15, Peron

QUIZ 20
SPORT

✁✁✁

1 Which runner made history by holding the world 800m, 1500m and mile records at the same time in 1979?

2 Whom did Bjorn Borg beat in 1979 to score his 4th Wimbledon men's singles title?

3 Was this losing finalist Australian, Canadian or American?

4 Which Spanish golfer took the 1979 British Open title?

5 What was Precious McKenzie's sport?

6 In which athletics event did Daley Thompson win international fame?

7 Which British runner set a world record over 2 miles in 1978?

8 What game was dominated by David Bryant?

9 Which soccer team won the First Division title in 1978?

10 Who was their manager?

11 In which sport did Gareth Edwards win fame before his retirement in 1978?

12 For which country was he an international star?

13 A cricket batsman scored 1000 runs before the end of May in 1973 (the first to do so since 1938). Who was he?

14 Which driver scored his record 26th Grand Prix win in the 1973 Dutch Grand Prix?

15 Who controversially beat boxer Henry Cooper in 1971?

✁✁✁

ANSWERS

1, Sebastian Coe 2, Roscoe Tanner 3, American 4, Severiano Ballesteros 5, Weightlifting 6, Decathlon 7, Steve Ovett 8, Bowls 9, Nottingham Forest 10, Brian Clough 11, Rugby Union 12, Wales 13, Glenn Turner (Worcestershire and New Zealand) 14, Jackie Stewart 15, Joe Bugner

QUIZ 21
PEOPLE

●●

1 What was the profession of Margaret Bourke-White, who died in 1971?

2 Gabrielle Chanel died in 1971. What was her nickname?

3 Of which country did Dom Mintoff become prime minister in 1971?

4 Charles Manson went on trial in 1970 for what crime?

5 In which year did Bernadette Devlin begin a prison sentence?

6 Who directed *Close Encounters of the Third Kind*?

7 Which Nobel prize did the scientist Andrey Sakharov win in 1979?

8 What was the title of Richard Attenborough's 1977 film about the Battle of Arnhem?

9 Who succeeded Pierre Trudeau as prime minister of Canada in 1979?

10 Which community was led by Rauf Denktash in the 70s?

11 Which western European dictator died in 1975?

12 Robert Altman directed a 1970 film about the Korean War. What was its title?

13 Of which country was Konstantinos Karamanlis prime minister?

14 James Laver died in 1975. He was a historian of what subject?

15 Of which country was Gaafar Nimeiry president through the 70s?

●●

ANSWERS

QUIZ 22
SCIENCE & TECHNOLOGY

1 In the early 70s television companies had to choose between which two colour systems?

2 Which Apollo mission was cut short by an explosion in an oxygen tank?

3 The U.S.S. Nimitz was commissioned in 1975: As what sort of ship?

4 Which crop fell victim in the 70s to the grassy stunt virus?

5 Which company was bankrupted by the cost of developing the RB-211 jet engine?

6 *Apollo14* was launched in 1971. Did it succeeed in landing on the Moon?

7 Which company took over the operation of most passenger trains in the U.S. in 1971?

8 In which country was the Rare Breeds Survival Trust founded?

9 Plans for a third London airport were shelved in 1974. Where was it then intended to be?

10 With which space station did *Soyuz* spacecraft dock in 1971?

11 The Tu-144 was first seen in the West in 1971. What was it?

12 In which year did the British government reduce the speed limit to 50 mph?

13 Which foreign seaweed became a problem in British waters in the 70s?

14 What did the MODE and POLYMODE programmes study?

15 During the 70s oil crisis some cars in Brazil used an unusual fuel. What was it?

ANSWERS

1, PAL and SECAM 2, Apollo 13 3, Nuclear-powered aircraft carrier 4, The Indonesian rice crop 5, Rolls-Royce Ltd. 6, Yes 7, Amtrak, the National Railroad Passenger Corporation 8, United Kingdom 9, On the Maplin Sands in the Thames estuary 10, Salyut 11, The Soviet supersonic jet airliner 12, 1974 13, Japanese seaweed, Sargassum muticum 14, Ocean eddies 15, Alcohol made from sugarcane

QUIZ 29
ARTS &
ENTERTAINMENT

1 The last of Richmal Crompton's children's books appeared in 1970. Who was the schoolboy hero ?

2 In which book do we meet Slartibartfast and Ford Prefect?

3 Who was the author?

4 How did this bestseller make its first appearance in 1978?

5 Complete the title of this 1974 bestseller: *Tinker, Tailor* …?

6 Who was its author?

7 Was the book's main character called George Smiley, Frederick Livesey, or Harry Palmer?

8 Which actor played this character in TV adaptations?

9 Which 70s bestseller described prisoners' efforts to escape from Devil's Island?

10 Can you name the author?

11 Who wrote a children's bestseller about rabbits?

12 What was it called?

13 Who wrote a 1971 book called *Adolf Hitler: My Part in His Downfall*?

14 Whose biography was entitled *The Moon's A Balloon*?

15 Which novelist wrote *Sweet William* (1975)?

ANSWERS

1. William (Brown) 2. *The Hitch Hiker's Guide to the Galaxy* 3. Douglas Adams 4. As a radio series on the BBC 5. *Soldier, Spy,* 6. John Le Carré 7. George Smiley 8. Alec Guinness 9. Papillon 10. Henri Charriere 11. Richard Adams 12. *Watership Down* 13. Spike Milligan 14. David Niven 15. Beryl Bainbridge

QUIZ 24
POT LUCK

••

1 What was the Beatles last single?

2 Who had a US number one with *War*?

3 In which country was racing driver Jochen Rindt killed?

4 Of which country was Salazar (died 1970) dictator?

5 Whose London grave was vandalized in 1970?

6 Where was it?

7 Who beat Jose Manuel Ibar to win a European title?

8 How old was the Queen Mother in 1970?

9 Who wrote the music for *Jesus Christ Superstar*?

10 Who wrote the lyrics?

11 What shocked audiences at its first unveiling at the Roundhouse in London?

12 Who died a month after being named chancellor of the exchequer?

13 What was Mick Jagger filming in Australia?

14 Was Pietro Annigoni a musician or a painter?

15 Who was the subject of a 1970 work by him?

••

ANSWERS

1. *Let It Be* (1970) 2. Edwin Starr 3. Italy 4. Portugal 5. Karl Marx 6. Highgate Cemetery 7. Henry Cooper 8. 70 9. Andrew Lloyd Webber 10. Tim Rice 11. Oh Calcutta! 12. Iain Macleod 13. *Ned Kelly* 14. A painter 15. The Queen (a portrait)

QUIZ 25
SPORT

••

1 What year did Arsenal win both the League and FA Cup?

2 Which world championship did Jackie Stewart win in 1971?

3 What did Chay Blyth do in 293 days ?

4 Was David Hemery an athlete known for his skill over hurdles, in the long jump pit, or in the pole vault?

5 In which sport were husband and wife John and Sheila Sherwood each successful?

6 A talented British runner, she died tragically of cancer in December 1970. Who was this "golden girl"?

7 Basil D'Oliveira was a star at which game?

8 He was picked to play for England, but where was D'Oliveira born?

9 Which Massechusetts city became famous for its Marathon?

10 Which "unknown" Australian woman won Wimbledon in 1971?

11 Was Mill Reef: a) the 1971 Derby winner b) the name of a racing yacht or c) the ground on which South Africa beat England at rugby?

12 J P R retired in 1979. Who was he?

13 In which sport was Scotland's Jim Watt a 1979 world champion?

14 Which Dutch soccer star was transferred from Ajax to Barcelona in 1973?

15 Which England and Man. Utd legend hung up his boots in 1973?

••

ANSWERS

1, 1971 2, World drivers' championship in Formula One 3, Sail around the world 4, He was a hurdler 5, Athletics 6, Lilian Board 7, Cricket 8, South Africa 9, Boston 10, Evonne Goolagong 11, a) 12, J P R Wiliiams – Welsh rugby union player 13, Boxing (lightweight) 14, Johann Cruyff 15, Bobby Charlton

QUIZ 26
WORLD EVENTS

1 Kalatdlit Nunat gained home rule in 1979. What is the more usual name for this island?

2 President Tombalbaye was deposed and killed in 1975: in which country?

3 Which two countries joined the EEC immediately after Britain?

4 What was the name of the 1973 agreement to end U.S. participation in the Vietnam War?

5 Which three countries claimed rights to the continental shelf around Rockall?

6 Where was Rockall?

7 Muhammad Daoud overthrew the monarchy of which country in 1973?

8 Who led the army rebellion in Chile in 1973?

9 Sir Seretse Khama won an election in 1979: in which republic?

10 Did Juan Peron ever return to power in Argentina in the 70s?

11 Who was the main Soviet signatory of SALT in 1972?

12 The Kilbrandon Commission reported in 1974: on what subject?

13 Which great U.S. city nearly went bankrupt in 1975?

14 Frolinat was active in Africa in the 70s. What was Frolinat?

15 In 1972, where did 'Black September' massacre Israeli athletes?

ANSWERS

1, Greenland 2, Chad 3, Ireland and Denmark 4, The Paris Agreement 5, The United Kingdom, Ireland and Denmark 6, It's a rock sticking out of the Atlantic Ocean 7, Afghanistan 8, General Augusto Pinochet 9, Botswana 10, Yes, he was elected president in 1973 11, Leonid Brezhnev 12, Devolution for Scotland and Wales 13, New York City 14, The Chad National Liberation Front 15, At the Olympic Games in Munich

QUIZ 27
PEOPLE

1 James Chichester-Clark resigned in 1971. What position had he held?

2 In 1979 Warren Mitchell played the part of Willy Loman in which Arthur Miller play?

3 Tilly Losch died in 1979. Was she a sculptress, a dancer, or an author?

4 In which country did Queen Margrethe come to the throne in 1972?

5 Who threatened a British writer with public execution for calling him a 'village tyrant'?

6 Who wrote *Bless the Bride* and *Misleading Cases*? He died in 1971.

7 What step did the Soviet dancer Mikhail Baryshnikov take in 1974?

8 Ross McWhirter, who was murdered in 1975, was co-editor of which best-seller?

9 Who was the Minister of Funny Walks in Monty Python?

10 Of which country did Suleyman Demirel become prime minister in 1975?

11 Audie Murphy, who died in 1971, played the hero in many films. Was he a real-life hero also?

12 Matyas Rakosi died in 1971. Which country had he dominated in earlier years?

13 In 1975 gymnast Nadia Comaneci found fame. From which country did she come?

14 Who returned to Iran in 1979 after 15 years of exile?

15 In which country was Cardinal Mindszenty primate?

ANSWERS

1, Prime minister of Northern Ireland 2, *Death of a Salesman* 3, A dancer 4, Denmark 5, Idi Amin 6, Sir Alan Herbert 7, He defected to the West 8, *The Guinness Book of Records* 9, John Cleese 10, Turkey 11, He won many decorations for bravery in World War II 12, Hungary 13, Romania 14, Ayatollah Khomeini 15, Hungary

QUIZ 28
WORLD EVENTS

•••

1 In which country was President Marien Ngouabi assassinated in 1977?

2 In which country was the Baader-Meinhof terrorist gang active in the 70s?

3 What was the name of the 1973 war between Egypt and Israel?

4 Which famous Dutch painting in Amsterdam was slashed in 1975?

5 Which cosmetics company introduced the Persian Roses look in 1975?

6 What was the Australian Army Reserve called before it was renamed?

7 What were the MBFR negotiations of the 70s about?

8 On which island did the "Mongoose Squad" operate in support of the police?

9 Which country did the National Redemption Council govern?

10 In which country was there a party in the 70s called the Awami League?

11 Which South American country strove in the 70s to gain access to the Pacific?

12 In which country were the three main liberation groups MPLA, UNITA and FNLA?

13 At which Scottish football ground were 66 people killed in 1971?

14 In which country did Tupamaro guerrillas kidnap the U.S. ambassador in 1971?

15 Which act of parliament regulated trade unions and collective bargaining in 1971?

•••

ANSWERS

1. Congo 2. West Germany 3. The Yom Kippur War 4. 'The Night Watch' 5. Helena Rubinstein 6. Citizen Military Forces 7. Mutual and balanced force reductions 8. Grenada 9. Ghana 10. Bangladesh 11. Bolivia 12. Angola 13. Ibrox Park, Glasgow 14. Uruguay 15. The Industrial Relations Act

POT LUCK

1 Who played a gangster called Devlin in *Performance*?

2 Who wrote the book on which the film *The Andromeda Strain* was based?

3 Which prime minister's wife published a book of poems in 1970?

4 What did Allen Lane (died 1970) do?

5 Which church decided yes to women ministers?

6 Who played a centenarian Indian in *Little Big Man*?

7 Who sang the title song to the *Aristocats*?

8 Which film told the story of Pearl Harbor?

9 Which famous racehorse died in 1970?

10 Where was Mrs Bandaranaike prime minister?

11 Who was the four-legged Nijinsky?

12 Who knocked England out of the 1970 World Cup?

13 Which British company launched its new four-wheel-drive all-road vehicle?

14 Who was the first actor to become a life peer in 1970?

15 Which famous novelist died in June 1970?

ANSWERS

1, James Fox 2, Michael Crichton 3, Mary Wilson 4, Published the first Penguin Books 5, Methodists 6, Dustin Hoffman 7, Maurice Chevalier 8, *Tora! Tora! Tora!* 9, Arkle 10, Ceylon (Sri Lanka) 11, A racehorse 12, West Germany 13, Rover (Range Rover) 14, Laurence Olivier 15, E. M. Forster

QUIZ 30
ARTS & ENTERTAINMENT

1 Whose last book was entitled *Curtain: Poirot's Last Case*?

2 Whose political diaries caused a stir among his Labour Party colleagues?

3 Who wrote *The Lord of the Rings* and died in 1973?

4 Which posthumous work by this author was labelled "Sellamillion" by satirists?

5 Cole Lesley, a valet, wrote a 1976 book about his employer ... who was?

6 Antonia Fraser wrote a 1973 biography subtitled ... *Our Chief of Men*. Who was the subject?

7 Which book about Ancient Rome by Robert Graves was a popular TV series?

8 Who played the leading role in this series, as the stammering Roman emperor?

9 Manuscripts of which 19th-century poets were found in a London bank vault in 1976?

10 Which Tom starred in the 1978 stage hit *Whose Life Is It Anyway?*: Conti, Courtney or Jones?

11 Which celebrated British poet died in 1973?

12 Whose memoirs were titled *At The End of the Day*?

13 In which city did LBC and Capital Radio begin broadcasting in 1973?

14 Which star of Fists of Fury died in 1973, aged only 32?

15 Poet Pablo Neruda, 1971 Nobel prizewinner, was from which country?

ANSWERS

1, Agatha Christie 2, Richard Crossman 3, J R R Tolkien 4, *The Silmarillion* 5, Noël Coward 6, Oliver Cromwell 7, *I Claudius* 8, Derek Jacobi 9, Shelley and Byron 10, Conti 11, W H Auden 12, Harold Macmillan 13, London 14, Bruce Lee 15, Chile

PEOPLE

• •

1 Elijah Muhammad died in 1975. Of which faith was he minister?

2 Who defeated Gerald Ford in the U.S. presidential election of 1976?

3 Of which country was General Mobutu president?

4 Who directed *The Bitter Tears of Petra von Kant* and *Fear Eats the Soul*?

5 Who became Britain's chancellor of the exchequer in 1974?

6 America's Sweetheart died in 1979. What was her name?

7 The author of *Not Waving But Drowning* died in 1971? Who was she?

8 The Pope visited Latin America in 1979. Which Pope was that?

9 Which former prime minister was hanged in Pakistan in 1979?

10 Dwight D Eisenhower's widow died in 1979. What was her first name?

11 Who played the lead role in *The French Connection*?

12 Jimmy Nervo died in 1975. Who was his partner in the *Crazy Gang*?

13 Who directed the 70s films *Il Decamerone* and *The Canterbury Tales*?

14 Airey Neave was killed by a car bomb in 1979. Where did it happen?

15 The president of Bangladesh was assassinated in 1975. What was his name?

• •

ANSWERS

1, Nation of Islam (Black Muslims) 2, Jimmy Carter 3, Zaire 4, Rainer Werner Fassbinder 5, Denis Healey 6, Mary Pickford 7, Stevie Smith 8, John Paul II 9, Zulfikar Ali Bhutto 10, Mamie 11, Gene Hackman 12, Teddy Knox 13, Pier Paolo Pasolini 14, On the way out of the underground garage of the House of Commons 15, "Mujibur Rahman, known as Sheikh Mujib"

POT LUCK

* * *

1 What fell on Scarborough in 1975?

2 What extra facial feature did Prince Charles grow?

3 Which Commonwealth country was he visiting at the time?

4 Who was chosen to lead the Conservative Party in 1975?

5 At which tube station in London did 35 people die in a crash?

6 Which US singer performed *Laughter in the Rain*?

7 Which famous West Indies cricketer was knighted in 1975?

8 What was the score in the 1975 FA Cup Final

9 Who beat whom in this game?

10 Which team was Bobby Moore playing for in the match?

11 How many runs did Graham Gooch sore in his first Test innings?

12 In which TV series did Fiona Fullerton play a trainee nurse?

13 Who starred as Polly in *Fawlty Towers*?

14 Whose autobiography was called *The Naked Civil Servant*?

15 Who starred in a TV adaptation of this book?

* * *

ANSWERS

1, A meteorite 2, A beard 3, Canada 4, Margaret Thatcher 5, Moorgate 6, Neil Sedaka 7, Gary Sobers 8, 2-0 9, West Ham beat Fulham 10, Fulham 11, A duck (0) 12, *Angels* 13, Connie Booth 14, Quentin Crisp 15, John Hurt

QUIZ 22
SCIENCE & TECHNOLOGY

1. What was studied by the *Helios 1* probe launched in 1974?
2. Combinatorics came to the fore in the 70s: in which branch of science?
3. Jolly Green Giants helped in the 1975 evacuation of Saigon. What were they?
4. Which country developed the Delta launch vehicle?
5. Which British rocket launched the Prospero satellite?
6. In which year was the first oil pumped from Britain's North Sea fields?
7. Which planet did *Mariner 9* orbit in 1971?
8. Which country launched it?
9. In 1975, which country had the biggest tonnage of merchant shipping?
10. In which year were pocket calculators first available?
11. Which U.S. airline was the first to offer services by jumbo jet, in 1970?
12. What was unusual about the main pavilion of Japan's Expo75?
13. MIRVs were fitted to intercontinental missiles in the 70s. What are they?
14. In which year did the Orient Express complete its last run between Paris and Istanbul?
15. Which important new railway started operating in Africa in 1975?

ANSWERS

1, The Sun, especially the solar wind 2, Mathematics 3, Helicopters 4, The United States 5, Black Arrow 6, 1975 7, Mars 8, The United States 9, Liberia 10, 1972 11, Pan Am 12, It was on a semi-submersible floating platform 13, Multiple independently targetable reentry vehicles 14, In 1977 15, Tanzam, the Tanzania-Zambia railway line

ARTS & ENTERTAINMENT

1 What was the nationality of writer Patrick White?

2 Was the 1977 BBC TV series *Wings* about World War I pilots, birds, or the pop band?

3 Which letter-writer wrote a bestseller about America in 1973?

4 Who was the author of the 1973 title *The Honorary Consul*?

5 Which artist designed sets for *The Rake's Progress* at the 1975 Glyndebourne opera?

6 In TV's *Upstairs, Downstairs* whom did Mr Hudson marry during the 1975 showing?

7 Which pop star was the subject of the 1972 film *Born to Boogie*?

8 Who starred alongside Woody Allen in the 1977 film *Annie Hall*?

9 What was Carl André's *Low* Sculpture (1976) at the Tate Gallery made of?

10 What was the "episode number" of the first *Star Wars* movie (1977)?

11 Who presented the TV series *Life on Earth*?

12 Which Edward was the subject of the television series *Edward and Mrs Simpson*?

13 Who starred in the 1973 movie *Lady Sings the Blues*?

14 Who was she playing?

15 With which singing group had she previously made her name?

ANSWERS

QUIZ 95
WORLD EVENTS

•••

1 General Yakubu Gowon was head of which country's military government?

2 In which year did the United Kingdom introduce decimal currency: 1971, 1975, or 1979?

3 The U.S. table tennis team started a thaw in international relations in 1971. How?

4 Which city was the scene of Bloody Sunday in 1972?

5 From which country in Africa were many Asians expelled in 1972?

6 Which country exploded its first nuclear device in 1974?

7 Why did Britain work a three-day week in 1974?

8 In which year did Turkey invade northern Cyprus?

9 What caused the collapse of the power-sharing Executive in Northern Ireland in 1974?

10 What was the consequence of the Guillaume spy affair for Willy Brandt?

11 Which organization, founded in Britain, won the 1977 Nobel prize for peace?

12 Who were the harkis who were not allowed to return to Algeria in the 70s?

13 The Democratic Republic of the Congo adopted a new name in 1971. What was it?

14 Thousands of Moroccans took part in a Green March in 1975: into which territory?

15 Surinam became independent in 1975. Which country previously ruled it?

•••

ANSWERS

1, Nigeria 2, 1971 3, They visited Communist China 4, Londonderry 5, Uganda 6, India 7, Because of fuel shortages 8, 1974 9, A general strike 10, It caused his resignation as chancellor 11, Amnesty International 12, Algerian soldiers who had fought on the side of the French 13, Zaire 14, Spanish Sahara 15, The Netherlands

QUIZ 36
SPORT

•••

1   In which sport was Heather McKay dominant?

2   Which Welsh cricketer captained England?

3   Which Australian swimmer won three gold medals at the Munich Olympics?

4   Where did the Chiefs play American football?

5   Which event did Mary Peters win at the 1972 Olympics?

6   At which weight did Ken Buchanan hold a world boxing title in 1970?

7   Was he a Scottish, Welsh or English fighter?

8   Who won cricket's first World Cup?

9   What year?

10 Whose winning streak did Luis Ocana break in 1973?

11 In which event?

12 For whom did Keith Stackpole play Test cricket?

13 What was the score in the 1970 World Cup final?

14 Which British team won the 1970 Cupwinners' Cup?

15 Which domestic trophy did they win the same year?

•••

ANSWERS

1, Squash, 2, Tony Lewis 3, Shane Gould 4, Kansas City 5, Pentathlon 6, Lightweight 7, Scottish 8, West Indies 9, 1975 10, Eddy Merckx 11, The Tour de France 12, Australia 13, 4-1 to Brazil 14, Manchester City 15, League Cup

QUIZ 97
ARTS &
ENTERTAINMENT

1 Where was a new Van Gogh Museum opened in 1973?

2 What year were museum charges introduced in the UK?

3 Which Egyptian king was the museum hit of 1972?

4 Which opera house staged its opening night in 1973?

5 What was the first opera staged there?

6 In 1973, the London Philharmonic were the first foreign orchestra to visit … where?

7 Who composed a new opera called *Death in Venice*?

8 Havergal Brian died in 1973; was he a composer, poet or painter?

9 With which Beatle did David Essex star in the film *That'll Be The Day*?

10 Who presented a music programme on radio called Baker's Dozen?

11 What job was he well known for doing on TV?

12 Which Michael gave up hosting radio's *Two Way Family Favourites* in 1970: a) Aspel b) Parkinson or c) Barrymore?

13 Which actor, who died in 1999, starred as US Army general George S Patton on screen?

14 The title of the film?

15 What was unusual about the actor's reaction to an Oscar award for his role?

ANSWERS

QUIZ 38
POT LUCK

●●●

1 Which British city was hit by IRA bombs in November 1974?

2 Where did Karamanlis become president?

3 Which former Secretary General of the United Nations died in 1974?

4 For which English club did Martin Buchan play soccer?

5 Which newspaper stopped its Saturday edition in 1974?

6 Which country cancelled plans to build a high speed train?

7 Which group sang *Seven Seas of Rhye*?

8 In which year did Wales not finish either first or second in the Five Nations rugby championship?

9 Which Australian city was damaged by a cyclone?

10 Which British MP disappeared from a beach in Miami?

11 Where did he reappear?

12 Who were *Lonely this Christmas* (on record)?

13 Who was British prime minister from October 1974?

14 Who had a hit with *Fernando*?

15 Which British prison was set on fire in autumn 1974?

●●●

ANSWERS

1. Birmingham 2. Greece 3. U Thant 4. Manchester United 5. The Evening Standard (London) 6. Britain 7. Queen 8. 1972 9. Darwin 10. John Stonehouse 11. Australia 12. Mud 13. Harold Wilson 14. Abba 15. The Maze

WORLD EVENTS

1 In Britain, which party won the most seats in the first general election of 1974?

2 Which year saw the fall of Pnom Penh and the end of the Pol Pot regime?

3 What new name did Dahomey adopt in 1975?

4 In which South American country did the MDB beat ARENA in the 1974 election?

5 Which Asian city had its entire population driven out into the countryside in 1975?

6 In 1975 terrorists burst into an OPEC meeting and took hostages: in which city?

7 In which country did the Janata Party win a landslide election victory in 1977?

8 In which year did Jeremy Thorpe resign as leader of the Liberal Party?

9 What do the initials SWAPO stand for?

10 From which organization was Egypt expelled in 1979?

11 In which year did voters in Wales reject devolution in a referendum?

12 SEATO was dissolved in 1977. What was it?

13 In which country was the head of state, General Mohammed, killed in 1976?

14 In which year in the 70s did the maharajahs of India lose most of their wealth and power?

15 In which country did the Sandinistas seize power in 1979?

ANSWERS

1, The Labour Party 2, 1979 3, Benin 4, Brazil 5, Pnom Penh 6, Vienna 7, India 8, 1976 9, South West Africa People's Organization 10, The Arab League 11, 1979 12, The Southeast Asia Treaty Organization 13, Nigeria 14, 1971 15, Nicaragua

PEOPLE

1 The composer of *The Firebird* and *The Rite of Spring* died in 1971. Who was he?

2 Who was prime minister of Japan from 1964 to 1972?

3 Basil Hume became a cardinal in 1976. Was he English, Welsh or Irish by birth?

4 Of which country was General Park Chung Hee president?

5 Who directed *Midnight Cowboy* and *Sunday, Bloody Sunday*?

6 The Queen's first grandson was born in 1977. Who was his mother?

7 R C Sherriff died in 1975. What was his best known play, about World War I?

8 Who played *Rhoda* in the televison series of that name?

9 When Anthony Crosland died in 1977, who succeeded him as foreign secretary?

10 What position did Walter Mondale attain in 1977?

11 Which musical film, based on Dickens, starred Albert Finney and Sir Alec Guinness?

12 Who was joint leader with Joshua Nkomo of the Patriotic Front of Zimbabwe?

13 Of which party was Brian Faulkner elected leader in 1971?

14 In 1971 Lt. William Calley was found guilty of murders in which Vietnamese village?

15 Who directed the 1971 film version of *Death in Venice*?

ANSWERS

1, Igor Stravinsky 2, Eisaku Sato 3, English 4, South Korea 5, John Schlesinger 6, Princess Anne 7, *Journey's End* 8, Valerie Harper 9, David Owen 10, Vice-president of the United States 11, *Scrooge* 12, Robert Mugabe 13, The Unionist Party in Northern Ireland 14, My Lai 15, Luchino Visconti

QUIZ 41
SPORT

1 Who was the first Open golf champion of the 70s?

2 In which sport did the Five Nations compete?

3 Which teams shared the Five Nations championship in 1970?

4 For which county did Mike Gatting play cricket?

5 In what sport did Tommy Nakajima feature as a winner?

6 What game did Roger Millward play?

7 In which sport did Great Britain beat Australia in 1970?

8 Which English socce team might have done the Treble, but failed in 1970?

9 Who did they beat in the FA Cup semi final?

10 And to whom did they lose the FA Cup Final?

11 Who thwarted them in the European Cup semi-final?

12 And who pipped them for the League title?

13 Who was their manager?

14 For whom did Mike Procter and Barry Richards star?

15 In which sport?

ANSWERS

1. Jack Nicklaus 2. Rugby Union 3. Wales and France 4. Middlesex 5. Golf 6. Rugby League 7. Rugby League 8. Manchester United 9. Leeds United (in 3 matches) 10. Chelsea 11. Celtic 12. Everton 13. Don Revie 14. South Africa 15. Cricket

QUIZ 42
WORLD EVENTS

1 In which year did the Soviet Union first send troops into Afghanistan?

2 Which country started a programme of Four Modernizations in the 70s?

3 The United Nations designated 1979 as the IYC. What did the initials stand for?

4 In which year did Saigon fall to North Vietnam?

5 Which capital city had a Democracy Wall in 1979?

6 In which country was the Charter 77 Declaration published?

7 Who led the 1979 revolution in Iran?

8 King Birendra succeeded King Mahendra in 1972: in which country?

9 In which country did Flight Lieutenant Jerry Rawlings come to power in 1979?

10 In which year did Iranian militants seize the U.S. embassy in Teheran?

11 In what way did the FLQ cause a national crisis in Canada in 1972?

12 Which Asian country seized the U.S. container ship Mayaguez in 1975?

13 In which year did Ireland join the European Community?

14 Which British photo-processing plant was the scene of a long industrial dispute in the 70s?

15 Whom did J R Jayawardene succeed as prime minister of Sri Lanka in 1977?

ANSWERS

1, 1979 2, China 3, International Year of the Child 4, 1975 5, Beijing 6, Czechoslovakia 7, Ayatollah Khomeini 8, Nepal 9, Ghana 10, 1979 11, They kidnapped two officials 12, Cambodia 13, 1973 14, Grunwick 15, Mrs Bandaranaike

ARTS &
ENTERTAINMENT

•••

1 What part did George C Scott play in the 1970 film *Jane Eyre*?

2 Which band recorded *Anarchy in the UK* (1976)?

3 Which Irish band lost three members killed in a terrorist ambush in 1975?

4 What was the English translation of the German band Kraftwerk's name?

5 Who sang *Whispering Grass*, a British number one of 1975?

6 On which TV show did these singers appear as actors in wartime garb?

7 Which band was on the run in 1974?

8 The creator of Jeeves died in 1975; who was he?

9 Who presented the first series of *Blankety Blank*?

10 Which actor starred in *Travesties* (1974)?

11 Who wrote *As If By Magic*?

12 Who presented *Royal Heritage* on television in 1977?

13 Whose volume of memoirs was called *Emlyn*?

14 Which actress made her name in the plays of *Samuel Beckett*?

15 Who starred as the female half of *Terry and June*?

•••

ANSWERS

1, Mr Rochester 2, The Sex Pistols 3, The Miami Showband 4, Power Plant 5, Don Estelle and Windsor Davies 6, *It Ain't 'Alf Hot, Mum* 7, Wings (with their hit *Band on the Run*) 8, P G Wodehouse 9, Terry Wogan 10, John Wood 11, Angus Wilson 12, Huw Wheldon 13, Emlyn Williams 14, Billie Whitelaw 15, June Whitfield

PEOPLE

* * *

1 Who was the interviewer in the BBC television series *Yesterday's Men*?

2 Which U.S. state governor was left paralyzed by an assassination attempt in 1972?

3 The composer Shostakovich died in 1975. What was his first name?

4 Sultan Qaboos came to the throne in 1970. In which country?

5 What post did Judith Hart hold, and then resign, in Harold Wilson's government?

6 Otto Skorzeny died in 1975. Whom did he rescue in 1943?

7 Gustav Husak became president of Czechoslovakia. Was he born a Czech or a Slovak?

8 What name did Reginald Kenneth Dwight adopt as a singer?

9 Harry S Truman died in 1972. Which was his home state?

10 Which union did Jack Jones lead?

11 For which kind of wrestling did Kitanoumi become famous?

12 P G Wodehouse died in 1975. What did the initials stand for?

13 The Gulag Archipelago was published in the West between 1973 and 1976. Who wrote it?

14 The author of *The Bridge of San Luis Rey* and *Our Town* died in 1975. Who was he?

15 The 200th anniversary of a famous ride fell in 1975. Who was the rider?

* * *

ANSWERS

1, David Dimbleby 2, George Wallace 3, Dmitry 4, Oman 5, Minister of Overseas Development 6, Benito Mussolini 7, Slovak 8, Elton John 9, Missouri 10, Transport and General Workers' Union 11, Sumo 12, Pelham Grenville 13, Alexander Solzhenitsyn 14, Thornton Wilder 15, Paul Revere

QUIZ 45
POT LUCK

●●●

1 What landed 362 passengers at Heathrow for the first time in January 1970?

2 Who was fined £200 for possession of cannabis in 1970?

3 Where did the 1970 winter 'flu outbreak come from?

4 What was happening in Mexico in 1970?

5 What event did Gay Trip win in 1970?

6 Which famous British philosopher died in February 1970?

7 Who acted as *A Question of Sport*'s first quizmaster?

8 In what TV programme did Frankie Howerd play a Roman slave?

9 Who were Tim, Graeme and Bill?

10 What were their full names?

11 Which Kenny was a DJ turned comedian?

12 Who were the *Family at War*?

13 Who starred in *Queenie's Castle*?

14 Where did demonstrators jeer President de Gaulle?

15 Which film gave John Wayne his first Oscar?

●●●

ANSWERS

1, A Boeing 747 (jumbo jet) 2, Mick Jagger 3, Hong Kong 4, The World Cup 5, The Grand National 6, Bertrand Russell 7, David Vine 8, *Up Pompeii* 9, *The Goodies* 10, Tim Brooke Taylor, Graeme Garden, Bill Oddie 11, Kenny Everett 12, The Ashtons 13, Diana Dors 14, Chicago 15, *True Grit*

QUIZ 46
SPORT

••

1   In which sport did the Chiefs beat the Vikings in 1970?

2   In which event did Ron Hill win European gold in 1970?

3   Who was Britain's first £200,000 footballer?

4   When did this transfer take place?

5   And between which clubs?

6   Which star striker went the other way as part of the deal?

7   What was first used in tennis in 1970?

8   Why did controversy at first surround it?

9   How did Ilie Nastase upset one umpore one time too many in 1970?

10 Was the World Cup rally for cars, bikes or aeroplanes?

11 What was Jochen Rindt's sport?

12 Which young Brazilian made his name in motor sport in 1970?

13 Which Grand Prix gave him his first win?

14 Who scored six times for Manchester United in the fifth round of the FA Cup (1970)?

15 Against whom?

••

ANSWERS

QUIZ 47
WORLD EVENTS

1 In which country did the Contras fight against the Sandinistas?

2 Was Spain's 1977 election won by the Democratic Centre or the Socialist Workers Party?

3 In which country did the Angry Brigade operate?

4 As the 70s ended, which was Britain's last island dependency in the Pacific?

5 When was Britain's first direct election for the European Parliament?

6 The widow of Mao Tse-tung was accused of belonging to a gang. What was it called?

7 The IMF set up a loan fund in 1977. What do the initials IMF stand for?

8 In which year did Margaret Thatcher become prime minister?

9 To which U.S. city did Laker Airways commence daily low-cost flights in 1977?

10 Papua New Guinea became independent in 1975. What is its capital called?

11 In which year did Pol Pot become premier of Cambodia?

12 By what other name was this country known?

13 Which international organization did the United States quit in 1977?

14 In which English city did the pub bombings take place in November 1974?

15 Was *Evita* first staged in London or in New York?

ANSWERS

1, Nicaragua 2, The Democratic Centre 3, In the United Kingdom 4, Pitcairn Island 5, 1979 6, The Gang of Four 7, International Monetary Fund 8, 1979 9, New York 10, Port Moresby 11, 1976 12, Kampuchea 13, ILO, the International Labour Organization 14, Birmingham 15, In London

QUIZ 48
SPORT

●●

1 Which Dutch team beat Celtic in the 1970 European Cup final?

2 Which horse was Nijinsky's sire?

3 What record did Nijinsky break in the 1970 Derby?

4 Which two other English races did it win to complete the Triple Crown?

5 Which division did boxer Carlos Monzon dominate in the early 70s?

6 Which martial arts had its first world champion in 1970?

7 From which country did he come?

8 Why was ice hockey difficult for the Sussex Senators?

9 Which ex-boxing champion was found dead of an overdode in December 1970?

10 Where were the first karate world championships held?

11 Whom did Muhammad Ali defeat in three rounds at Atlanta in a comeback fight in October 1970?

12 How long had he been out of the ring?

13 Why?

14 Which "unstoppable" Argentinian did Ali then beat over 15 rounds?

15 Which boxer did he have to beat to regain his title?

●●

ANSWERS

1. Feyenoord 2. Northern Dancer 3. The course record 4. Two Thousand Guineas and St Leger 5. Middleweight 6. Kendo 7. Japan 8. They had no home ice rink 9. Sonny Liston 10. Tokyo 11. Jerry Quarry 12. Three and a half years 13. He had been stripped of his title for refusing to join the US military 14. Oscar Bonavena 15. Joe Frazier

QUIZ 49
PEOPLE

comseses comseses comseses comseses comseses

1 In which Washington scandal were J D Ehrlichman and H R Haldeman involved?

2 Who rode The Minstrel to victory in the 1977 Derby?

3 In which year did General Franco die?

4 Who went to Oslo to accept Andrey Sakharov's Nobel prize?

5 What position did Andrey Gromyko hold in the Soviet government in the 70s?

6 James Hoffa went missing in 1975. He had been president of which U.S. union?

7 Mother Seton was declared a saint in 1975. In which city was she born in 1774?

8 In which country was Oginga Odinga a political leader?

9 Who succeeded Iain Macleod as chancellor of the exchequer in 1970?

10 Angela Rippon found fame by reading the television news: for the BBC or for ITN?

11 Which alliance headed by Malcolm Fraser won the 1975 election in Australia?

12 Who wrote the 70s plays *Equus* and *Amadeus*?

13 Antonio Salazar died in 1970. Which country did he rule for 40 years?

14 What post did Roy Jenkins take up in 1977?

15 Oleg Protopopov defected to the West in 1979. Was he a figure skater or a dancer?

comseses comseses comseses comseses comseses

ANSWERS

15, A figure skater
13, Portugal 14, President of the Commission of the European Community
BBC evening news 11, The Liberal-Country Party alliance 12, Peter Shaffer
minister 6, Teamsters 7, New York 8, Kenya 9, Anthony Barber 10, She read the
1, Watergate 2, Lester Piggott 3, 1975 4, His wife, Yelena Bonner 5, Foreign

WORLD EVENTS

1 Why did China invade Vietnam in 1979?

2 Jack Lynch scored an election victory in 1977. Which party did he lead?

3 A new museum was opened in London in 1976. What is its name?

4 In which country did Charles Joseph Clark become prime minister in 1979?

5 Libya adopted a new flag in 1977. What is unusual about it?

6 Of which country did General Geisel become president in 1974?

7 Which 'new wave' swept the pop music business in 1977?

8 Which country did Israel invade in 1978?

9 Fiji and Tonga gained full independence in 1970, 1975, or 1979. Which is correct?

10 Festac 2 was held in Nigeria in 1977. What did the name 'Festac' stand for?

11 At which airport did an Israeli commando unit rescue 100 hostages in 1976?

12 In which year did Portuguese rule in Angola end?

13 In which country did Charter 77 demand human rights?

14 What was the subject of the international agreement made in Helsinki in 1975?

15 In which country is Helsinki?

ANSWERS

1, In response to Vietnam's invasion of Cambodia 2, Fianna Fail 3, The Museum of London 4, Canada 5, It is a plain green rectangle 6, Brazil 7, Punk rock 8, Lebanon 9, 1970 10, World Black and African Festival of Arts and Culture 11, Entebbe in Uganda 12, 1975 13, Czechoslovakia 14, Human rights 15, Finland

QUIZ 51
ARTS & ENTERTAINMENT

1 Who married Kathy Silva on stage in New York in 1974?

2 Who had a 1974 hit with *The Streak*?

3 How did Keith Moon die in 1978?

4 Which duo hit the charts in 1978 with *Summer Nights*?

5 *We Don't Talk Anymore* was a 1979 hit for who?

6 Which band released an album titled *Regatta De Blanc* in 1979?

7 And who sang *Dancing Queen* in 1977?

8 For which group did Phil Collins take over from Peter Gabriel as lead singer?

9 With which 70s band did Eric Faulkner play guitar?

10 Johnny Rotten and Sid Vicious were members of which punk band?

11 Whose record of *Bohemian Rhapsody* topped the British charts in 1976?

12 Who came back to the charts in 1972 with *My Ding A Ling*?

13 With whom did John Lennon make his last stage appearance in New York on November 28, 1974?

14 Which US Presidential candidate claimed to have been inspired by the Beatles and Bob Dylan?

15 What was the title of Deniece Williams' 1977 UK chart-topper?

ANSWERS

1, Sly Stone 2, Ray Stevens 3, Accidental drug overdose 4, John Travolta and Olivia Newton-John 5, Cliff Richard 6, The Police 7, ABBA 8, Genesis 9, Bay City Rollers 10, The Sex Pistols 11, Queen 12, Chuck Berry 13, Elton John 14, Jimmy Carter (in 1976) 15, Free

QUIZ 52
POT LUCK

●●

1 Who played Mr Abbott in *Bless This House*?

2 Which Peter starred in *The Onedin Line*?

3 Who sang *One Bad Apple* in 1971?

4 What happened on 15th February 1971?

5 Which African country did Princess Anne visit in 1970?

6 In which country did Milton Obote lose his job?

7 In which European country did people riot in 1970 over food prices?

8 Which 1970s glamour competition was disrupted by demonstrators?

9 In which country did 146 people die in a 1970 dance hall fire?

10 For whom did Felix play soccer in 1970?

11 Who starred with 10 goals for West Germany in the 1970 World Cup?

12 Who kept goal for England in their last World Cup '70 match?

13 Where was the Pope attacked with a knife?

14 Where did Gay Liberation stage its first British demonstration?

15 Where did Arabella the spider spin shapeless webs in 1971?

●●

ANSWERS

1, Sid James 2, Peter Gilmore 3, The Osmonds 4, Decimalization 5, Kenya 6, Uganda 7, Poland 8, Miss World 9, France 10, Brazil 11, Gerd Muller 12, Peter Bonetti 13, The Philippines 14, London 15, In space, on board the US Skylab

QUIZ 59
SPORT

✎✎✎

1 Where did the 1970 Fight of Champions take place?

2 Which fighter's nickname was Smokin' Joe?

3 Whom did he beat in this fight?

4 Who was the joker on the 70s golf circuit?

5 Which cricketer made a century on his debut for Australia in 1970?

6 Whom did Margaret Court beat to win the 1970 US singles title?

7 Did she achieve the Grand Slam this year?

8 Who was the only woman before her to have done this?

9 Whose cricker tour of England was cancelled?

10 Which team stepped in to play England?

11 Who captained this side?

12 What was the score in the five match series?

13 Whom did Bob Taylor replace as England wicket keeper?

14 Against whom did the recalled Knott then score 101?

15 And how many did he score in the second innings of the same match?

✎✎✎

ANSWERS

1, Madison Square Garden 2, Joe Frazier 3, Muhammad Ali, on points 4, Lee Trevino 5, Greg Chappell 6, Rosie Casals 7, Yes 8, Maureen Connolly (1953) 9, South Africa 10, The Rest of the World 11, Gary Sobers 12, 4-1 to the Rest of the World 13, Alan Knott 14, New Zealand 15, 96

QUIZ 54
WORLD EVENTS

1. In which year did the UN Security Council order an arms embargo against South Africa?

2. Which Egyptian leader addressed the Israeli Knesset (parliament) in 1977?

3. In which year did Indonesia invade East Timor?

4. What new name did Cambodia adopt in 1976?

5. In China Mao Tse-tung and premier Chou En-lai died in the same year. Which year?

6. In 1976 Seychelles became an independent republic. Did it remain in the Commonwealth?

7. What name was adopted by the Gilbert Islands on becoming independent in 1979?

8. In 1970s Guyana, which party was led by Cheddi Jagan?

9. Divorce was legalized in 1970 and abortion in 1978: in which country?

10. In 1976 Cuba sent soldiers to fight in the civil war in which African country?

11. In which country was the Shah overthrown in 1979?

12. In which year did the United Kingdom join the European Community?

13. Which dictatorship in western Europe was overthrown in 1974?

14. ECOWAS was launched in 1976 and led by Nigeria and Ivory Coast. What was it?

15. What name was taken by Portuguese Guinea when it became independent in 1974?

ANSWERS

QUIZ 55
PEOPLE

cccccccccccccccccccccccccccccccccccccccccccc

1. Who starred as the boxer in the film *Rocky*?

2. In which country did Kim Young Sam lead the opposition party?

3. Can you give the first name of the film director Kurosawa?

4. To what United Nations post was General Odd Bull appointed in 1970?

5. In which country did Felix Malloum become head of state in 1975?

6. Who was head of the Metropolitan Police at the time of the Spaghetti House siege?

7. Who wrote *Flashman in the Great Game*, which was published in 1975?

8. Which party did Joshua Nkomo lead in 70s Rhodesia?

9. Which game did Prince Alexis Obolensky make popular in the 70s?

10. Of which country was Suleiman Franjieh elected president in 1970?

11. Aristotle Onassis named his yacht after his daughter. Her name?

12. Which famous lady had Onassis married in the 60s?

13. Which two actors starred in the 1970 BBC television serial *The Roads to Freedom*?

14. For what activity did Tom Keating become well known in the mid-70s?

15. What temporary post did Lord Soames take up in Africa in 1979?

cccccccccccccccccccccccccccccccccccccccccccc

ANSWERS

WORLD EVENTS

●●

1 CARICOM was set up in 1973. What is it?

2 Of which country did Jose Lopez Portillo become president in 1976?

3 Which ballet company celebrated its 200th birthday in 1976?

4 In which country did the UNITA guerillas operate in the 70s?

5 In 1975 the Pathet Lao seized control of which country?

6 What did the abbreviation SALT stand for in 70s diplomacy?

7 In which year did North Vietnam finally overrun South Vietnam?

8 What is meant by the initials PLA in China?

9 In which year did Harold Wilson's government make a social contract with the TUC?

10 In Denmark, what is meant by the Folketing?

11 Under what name did the Territory of the Afars and Issas become independent?

12 In which year did the Suez Canal reopen after the wars with Israel?

13 In New Zealand, which party was in power from 1972 to 1975?

14 What natural disaster struck Guatemala in 1976: earthquakes or a tidal wave?

15 SELA was established in 1975. What was it?

●●

ANSWERS

1. The Caribbean Common Market 2. Mexico 3. The Bolshoi Ballet 4. Angola 5. Laos 6. Strategic Arms Limitation Talks 7. 1975 8. The People's Liberation Army 9. 1974 10. The Danish parliament 11. Djibouti 12. 1975 13. The Labour Party 14. Earthquakes 15. The Latin-American Economic System

QUIZ 57
POT LUCK

●●●

1 Who were the Bellamys?

2 Who married Margaret Sinclair?

3 Who made an album called *Pictures at an Exhibition*?

4 Where was President Levington deposed?

5 Whose *Hot Love* reached number 1 in 1971?

6 Who sang *Gypsies, Tramps and Thieves*?

7 Where in Europe did women get the right to vote in 1971?

8 Where was Erich Honecker the man in charge?

9 Who married a beauty called Bianca in 1971?

10 Who led British negotiations with the EEC?

11 Which part of Pakistan broke away to become independent in 1971?

12 What new name did it adopt?

13 For which British city was the Barbican Arts centre planned?

14 Which three Arab nations joined in a federation in 1971?

15 With what unusual crime was Joyce McKinney charged in 1978?

●●●

ANSWERS

1, The Upstairs family in Upstairs Downstairs 2, Pierre Trudeau 3, Emerson, Lake and Palmer 4, Argentina 5, T Rex 6, Cher 7, Switzerland 8, East Germany 9, Mick Jagger 10, Geoffrey Rippon 11, East Pakistan 12, Bangladesh 13, London 14, Syria, Egypt and Libya 15, Kidnapping a Mormon missionary

ARTS &
ENTERTAINMENT

1 How was Elton John immortalized in 1976?

2 Which 70s musician was married to actress Carrie Snodgrass?

3 What year was the first Reading Festival in the UK?

4 Who declared that 1973 had seen his last live show but was back 12 months later?

5 What was the name of the 1973 chart-topping band led by ex-Move guitarist Roy Wood?

6 Complete the band names: Deep …

7 Led …?

8 What was the *British Re-Invasion Show* of 1973?

9 Whose debut album in 1977 was called *My Aim Is True*?

10 Whose *Shadow Dancing* was an US hit of summer 1977?

11 By what name was former singer Cat Stevens known at the time of his marriage in London in 1979?

12 Which British group recorded *Rat Trap* (1978)?

13 Which member of this band went on to achieve international fame as a charity fund-raiser?

14 Which 70s singer was married to Rita Coolidge (1973)?

15 Who recorded the 1975 *Natty Dread* album?

ANSWERS

1, He had his own waxwork dummy in Madame Tussauds 2, Neil Young 3, 1973 4, David Bowie 5, Wizzard 6, Purple 7, Zeppelin 8, A US tour by 60s groups including Herman's Hermits and Gerry and the Pacemakers… 9, Elvis Costello 10, Andy Gibb 11, Yusef Islam 12, The Boomtown Rats 13, Bob Geldof 14, Kris Kristofferson 15, Bob Marley

PEOPLE

•••

1   Who wrote *Looking for Mr. Goodbar*?

2   Of which country was Michael Manley prime minister in the 70s?

3   What post did Merlyn Rees hold in Harold Wilson's 1974 government?

4   Which cellist announced in 1975 that he would remain away from the Soviet Union?

5   Who directed the 1975 film *Rollerball*?

6   Which member of parliament disappeared from a Florida beach in 1974?

7   In which country was the composer Malcolm Williamson born?

8   Josephine Baker died in 1975. Which was her adopted country?

9   Who was Jimmy Carter's running mate in the 1976 presidential election?

10 Who directed the 1975 film *Jaws*?

11 Who succeeded U Thant in 1972 as secretary-general of the United Nations?

12 Avery Brundage died in 1975. Of which organization was he president?

13 Nikolay Bulganin died in 1975. With whom had he shared power in the Soviet Union?

14 Who wrote *The Honorary Consul*, published in 1973?

15 Why were 'Moonies' so called in the 70s?

•••

ANSWERS

1, Judith Rossner 2, Jamaica 3, Secretary of state for Northern Ireland 4, Mstislav Rostropovich 5, Norman Jewison 6, John Stonehouse 7, Australia 8, France 9, Walter Mondale 10, Steven Spielberg 11, Kurt Waldheim 12, The International Olympic Committee 13, Nikita Khrushchev 14, Graham Greene 15, After the Reverend Sun Myung Moon

POT LUCK

- **1** Where was Papa Doc president?
- **2** Who took over from him when he died in 1971?
- **3** And his nickname was?
- **4** How did the *Daily Mail* change in 1971?
- **5** Who sang *Joy to the World*?
- **6** What was new about a trip to the Natural History Museum in 1971?
- **7** Where was the *Mariner 9* spacecraft sent to?
- **8** Which English soccer team did the double in 1971?
- **9** Who came second to this team in the League?
- **10** And which team did they beat in the FA Cup Final?
- **11** Which horse won the Derby in 1971?
- **12** What kind of craft was HMS *Artemis*?
- **13** What happened to it in Portsmouth harbour?
- **14** What did British motorcyclists have to wear by law?
- **15** Where did King Hassan put down a coup?

ANSWERS

1, Haiti 2, His son 3, Baby Doc 4, It went tabloid 5, Three Dog Night 6, Museum charges were introduced 7, Mars 8, Arsenal 9, Leeds 10, Liverpool 11, Mill Reef 12, A submarine 13, It sank 14, Helmets 15, Morocco

QUIZ 61
SCIENCE & TECHNOLOGY

1 Which country maintained Syowa Station in Antarctica?

2 In 1975 an Apollo spacecraft linked up with which type of Soviet spacecraft?

3 Which French carmaker did Peugeot take over in 1974?

4 A tower 1815 feet tall (including antenna) was completed in 1975: in which city?

5 Cray 1 cost $8 million in 1979. Whatever was it?

6 In which country was a hominid skull 2,500,000 years old discovered in 1972?

7 In which year did home video recorders come on the market?

8 On which continent did the international Dry Valley Drilling Project take place?

9 Conservation of the site of Mohenjo-daro was carried out. In which country is it?

10 Which two Asian countries launched their first satellite in 1970?

11 In which country was the Auburn Dam built in the 70s?

12 What is the name of the highway from Alaska to Tierra del Fuego?

13 Which new disease was diagnosed in 1977?

14 What is the function of Marisat satellites?

15 Which country built the Leopard tank?

ANSWERS

1, Japan 2, Soyuz 3, Citroën 4, Toronto 5, A supercomputer 6, Kenya 7, 1975 8, Antarctica 9, Pakistan 10, China and Japan 11, United States 12, Pan-American Highway 13, AIDS 14, Ship-to-shore communication 15, Germany

QUIZ 62
ARTS & ENTERTAINMENT

1 Who sang *American Pie* (1971)?

2 Blondie was formed in 1975; who was the band's lead singer?

3 Who was the *Divine Miss M* – the title of her first album (1972)?

4 Who recorded *Bat Out Of Hell* (1978)?

5 Where did *Love Grow* in a 1970 hit?

6 Who had a 1978 hit with *Hit Me With Your Rhythmn Stick*?

7 Which member of the Doors died in July 1971 in Paris?

8 Which guitarist was also the lead singer of Derek and the Dominoes in 1970?

9 What year did Marc Bolan of T Rex die?

10 Which 70s band featured Francis Rossi?

11 Which 70s singer made the headlines for her romance with California Governor Jerry Brown?

12 Who reissued *Baby Love* in 1974?

13 Who sang *Summer Nights* in 1978?

14 Who got to number 4 in the UK with *Jack In The Box* in 1971?

15 Who were behind Garnet Mimms – a 1977 one-hit wonder?

ANSWERS

1, Don McLean 2, Debbie Harry 3, Bette Midler 4, Meat Loaf 5, *Where My Rosemary Goes* 6, Ian Dury and the Blockheads 7, Jim Morrison 8, Eric Clapton 9, 1977 10, Status Quo 11, Linda Ronstadt 12, The Supremes 13, John Travolta and Olivia Newton-John 14, Clodagh Rogers 15, Truckin' Co

QUIZ 69
WORLD EVENTS

1 In which country did the Symbionese Liberation Army operate?

2 Were the Phalangist forces in the civil war in Lebanon Muslim or Christian?

3 In which year was the Pol Pot regime in Cambodia brought to an end?

4 In British local government, what bodies took over in 1975 from Scottish counties and burghs?

5 Which European country gave women the vote in 1971?

6 Which tabloid did Express Newspapers launch in 1978?

7 What was Gan Island in the Maldives used for until 1975?

8 Which organization fought for the independence of the former Spanish Sahara?

9 Which British colony declared itself a republic in 1970?

10 From which country did the boat people come in the late 70s?

11 In which country was Cardinal Sin archbishop?

12 In which year did Britain's National Theatre vacate the Old Vic?

13 Which was the first homeland to be declared independent in South Africa?

14 Which organization proclaimed 1975–85 as the Decade for Women?

15 The status of Sikkim changed in 1975. What did it become?

ANSWERS

1, The United States 2, Christian 3, 1979 4, Regional and islands councils 5, Switzerland 6, *The Daily Star* 7, It was a Royal Air Force staging post 8, Polisario 9, Rhodesia 10, Vietnam 11, The Philippines 12, 1976 13, Transkei 14, The United Nations 15, One of the states of India

QUIZ 64
SPORT

1 Which Yorkshire captain was dismissed in the winter of 70-71?

2 Which star of the future hit his first runs for India in Trinidad?

3 Which lowly team beat Leeds 3-2 in the FA Cup?

4 Who hit a six iron on the Moon?

5 What game did the Murrayfield Racers play?

6 Who bought Brabham Cars?

7 Was John Snow a cricketer, a rugby player or a tennis star?

8 Where was he assailed by flying beer cans?

9 Why?

10 What was Rodney Marsh's role in the Australian cricket team?

11 Whom did Bertie Mee manage?

12 Why did England and Australia play a one-day game at Melbourne?

13 Who won this first-ever one-day international?

14 Which team won rugby's Grand Slam in 1971?

15 Who was their star fly-half?

ANSWERS

1. Brian Close 2. Sunil Gavaskar 3. Colchester United 4. Alan Shepard 5. Ice hockey 6. Bernie Ecclestone 7. Cricketer 8. Australia 9. He had hit an Australian player with a fast delivery 10. Wicketkeeper 11. Arsenal 12. Rain had washed out the first 3 days of play 13. Australia 14. Wales 15. Barry John

ARTS & ENTERTAINMENT

1 Complete this 1970 group: Edison …?

2 Who sang *Wandrin' Star*?

3 Which film was this song from?

4 Which tough-guy movie actor co-starred in the film?

5 Which song did he record on the B side of *Wandrin' Star*?

6 Which duo built a *Bridge over Troubled Water*?

7 What were their real names?

8 Which was their last album as a duo in the70s?

9 Which of them went into the movies for a time?

10 Who recorded the 1970 hit *Spirit In The Sky*?

11 What was his follow-up hit?

12 Did he record under his own name?

13 Who sang *Back Home* in 1970?

14 What song was a June 1970 hit for Mungo Jerry?

15 Where did their name come from?

ANSWERS

1, Lighthouse 2, Lee Marvin 3, *Paint Your Wagon* 4, Clint Eastwood 5, I Talk To The Trees 6, Simon and Garfunkel 7, Paul Simon and Arthur Garfunkel 8, *Bridge Over Troubled Water* 9, Art Garfunkel 10, Norman Greenbaum 11, He never had another hit 12, Yes 13, The England World Cup squad 14, *In the Summertime* 15, A cat in one of T S Eliot's verses

POT LUCK

1 Where did Charles Haughey become prime minister?

2 Which Asian country did the USSR invade in 1979?

3 Which group sang *Babe*?

4 Why was the Shah on the move in 1979?

5 Where did he eventually find a refuge?

6 Who won the 1979 Nobel Peace Prize?

7 In which city did she do her work?

8 In which country was she born?

9 Which group had a hit with *Another Brick in the Wall*?

10 Who won the US Open Golf title for the first time in 1979?

11 Who set a world record for the 800 metres in 1979?

12 In which city was this record run?

13 For whom did Alan Sunderland score the winner in the 1979 FA Cup Final?

14 Who was revealed as the "fourth man" in a spy scandal?

15 Which group of British workers demanded a 65 per cent pay rise in 1979?

ANSWERS

1. Republic of Ireland 2. Afghanistan 3. Styx 4. He had been deposed in Iran 5. Panama 6. Mother Teresa 7. Calcutta 8. Albania 9. Pink Floyd 10. Fuzzy Zoeller 11. Sebastian Coe 12. Oslo 13. Arsenal 14. Anthony Blunt 15. Coal miners

QUIZ 67
WORLD EVENTS

- **1** The 1978 mass suicide of the followers of Jim Jones took place in which country?
- **2** Which U.S. aircraft corporation was accused in 1976 of bribery in several countries?
- **3** Which South American country nationalized its oil industry in January 1976?
- **4** In what year was the European Monetary System formed?
- **5** Which city became the capital of the unified state of Vietnam?
- **6** Why did several Arab nations break off relations with Egypt in 1979?
- **7** Which two countries were in dispute about the Beagle Islands?
- **8** In which country was UNIFIL stationed?
- **9** In 1979 Britain closed its military base in which Mediterranean island republic?
- **10** Which national daily newspaper in London suspended publication for most of 1979?
- **11** Which two countries applied in 1977 to join the European Economic Community?
- **12** Which Middle East country nationalized the foreign-operated oil industry in 1973?
- **13** In 1973 the Partido Revolucionario Institucional won elections: in which country?
- **14** What name was chosen for Japan's armed forces?
- **15** Under what name did the Trucial States become fully independent in 1971?

ANSWERS

1, Guyana 2, Lockheed 3, Venezuela 4, 1979 5, Hanoi 6, Egypt had signed a treaty with Israel 7, Chile and Argentina 8, In Lebanon 9, Malta 10, *The Times* 11, Portugal and Spain 12, Iran 13, Mexico 14, Self-Defence Forces 15, United Arab Emirates

QUIZ 68
PEOPLE

1 Did Garry Trudeau create Doonesbury or was he prime minister of Canada?

2 Who wrote the 70s plays *No Man's Land* and *Betrayal*?

3 Of which country did Robert Muldoon become prime minister in 1975?

4 Who played the lead part in *Shampoo*?

5 Of which party did David Steel become leader in 1976?

6 Chiang Kai-shek died in 1975. On which island did he take refuge in 1949?

7 Of which country was Odvar Nordli prime minister in the 70s?

8 The king of Saudi Arabia was assassinated in 1975. What was his name?

9 Eamon de Valera died in 1975. In which city was he born?

10 Michael Flanders died in 1975. Was it Flanders or Swann who played the piano?

11 How old was Harold Wilson when he resigned as prime minister in 1976?

12 Sir Stanley Baker died in 1976. Was he English, Scottish or Welsh by birth?

13 In which year did the black South African leader Steve Biko die in custody?

14 Who wrote Pennies from Heaven, seen on television in 1978?

15 Which Pope held the fifth synod of Roman Catholic bishops in 1977?

ANSWERS

1. He created the Doonesbury comic strip 2. Harold Pinter 3. New Zealand 4. Warren Beatty 5. The Liberal Party 6. Taiwan 7. Norway 8. Faisal 9. New York 10. Donald Swann 11. Sixty years old 12. Welsh 13. 1977 14. Dennis Potter 15. Pope Paul VI

QUIZ 69
SPORT

1 How many Welsh players were picked for the 1971 Lions tour to New Zealand?

2 Who captained the Welsh team, and the British Lions?

3 Who was the Welsh team's formidable scrum half?

4 Which tennis star's name meant "tall trees by still water"?

5 Who arrived at Liverpool from Scunthorpe in 1971?

6 Who said: "My family was so poor ... the lady next door had me"?

7 Which year did he win both the US and "British" championships?

8 How did Wimbledon's first tie break differ from everyone else's?

9 What was Zaheer Abbas's sport?

10 For whom did he play internationally?

11 Who played his 114th and final Test in 1971?

12 For whom did Bob Wilson keep goal in the 1971 Cup Final?

13 Whom did his team beat?

14 Who scored the winning goal?

15 What double did this bring the winners?

ANSWERS

1. 13 (of 30) 2. John Dawes 3. Gareth Edwards 4. Evonne Goolagong's 5. Kevin Keegan 6. Lee Trevino 7. 1971 (US Open and Open) 8. It began at 8-8, not 6-6 when first introduced in 1971 9. Cricket 10. Pakistan 11. Colin Cowdrey 12. Arsenal 13. Liverpool 2-1 14. Charlie George 15. English League and Cup double

QUIZ 70
WORLD EVENTS

ccccccccccccccccccccccccccccccccccccccccccccccccccc

1 In which year did direct rule begin in Northern Ireland: 1972, 1974, or 1976?

2 To which country did the U.S. return the southern Ryukyus in 1972?

3 Dominica was ravaged by Hurricane David in 1979. Is Dominica in the Commonwealth?

4 Which battle site was occupied in 1973 by the American Indian Movement?

5 In which British colony was the governor assassinated in 1973?

6 In the 1973 war against Egypt, did the Israeli army cross the Suez Canal?

7 Which U.S. television show was based on *Till Death Us Do Part*?

8 In which year did the Bahamas become independent: 1973, 1976, or 1979?

9 Which London fashion house introduced a Denim Range of cosmetics?

10 What was the result of a shortage of glass bottles in Britain in 1973?

11 With which country did the Federal Republic of Germany make the Basic Treaty?

12 Which act of parliament required local housing authorities to charge a fair rent?

13 Which form of corporal punishment was practised by the Isle of Man in the 70s?

14 In which country did extremists kill 430 people by setting light to a cinema in 1978?

15 What charge did the Bingham Report lay against two British oil companies?

ccccccccccccccccccccccccccccccccccccccccccccccccccc

ANSWERS

Rhodesia

violent offenders 14, Iran 15, That they had broken the sanctions against
Democratic Republic 12, The Housing Finance Act, 1972 13, Birching of young,
9, Biba 10, Dairies used more paper and plastic containers 11, The German
Republic is not 4, Wounded Knee 5, Bermuda 6, Yes 7, *All in the Family* 8, 1973
1, 1972 2, Japan 3, Dominica is in the Commonwealth but the Dominican

QUIZ 71
ARTS &
ENTERTAINMENT

1 Who sang about a yellow river in 1970?

2 Which was the largest vocal chart-topping group this year?

3 Who sang *The Wonder Of You*?

4 In which US city was it recorded live?

5 Who backed Smokey Robinson?

6 What song took him and them into the 1970 charts?

7 What was Smokey's real first name?

8 On which label did he record?

9 Who was singing about a *Band of Gold* this year?

10 Who wrote a song called *Woodstock*?

11 And who had a 1970 hit with it in the UK?

12 *Voodoo Chile* was a hit for …?

13 Who wrote the song?

14 What happened to him on 18 September 1970?

15 Who sang *I Hear You Knockin'* ?

ANSWERS

1. Christie, 2. The England World Cup squad 3. Elvis Presley 4. Las Vegas 5. The Miracles 6. *Tears of a Clown* 7. William 8. *Motown* 9. Freda Payne 10. Joni Mitchell 11. Matthews' Southern Comfort 12. Jimi Hendrix Experience 13. Jimi Hendrix 14. He died 15. Dave Edmunds

QUIZ 72
PEOPLE

- **1** Who directed the film *Star Wars*?
- **2** Dame Barbara Hepworth died in 1975. Was she known for painting or for sculpture?
- **3** In which year did President Nasser die?
- **4** How did the Japanese writer Yukio Mishima die in 1970?
- **5** Who was U.S. president when Spiro T Agnew was vice-president?
- **6** Who wrote the song *Raindrops Keep Fallin' on My Head*?
- **7** Which party in Germany did Willy Brandt lead?
- **8** Who played Hercule Poirot in the 1975 film of *Murder on the Orient Express*?
- **9** Did the racing driver Graham Hill die in an air accident or in a car crash?
- **10** Which former Italian premier was kidnapped by the Red Brigades in 1978?
- **11** The *Silmarillion* was published posthumously in 1977. Who wrote it?
- **12** In 1979 Rhodesia had its first black prime minister. Who was he?
- **13** On which country did Emilio Colombo become prime minister in 1970?
- **14** What was novel about Emperor Hirohito's visit to Europe in 1971?
- **15** The author of *Mathematics for the Million* died in 1975. His name?

ANSWERS

1. George Lucas 2. For her sculptures 3. 1970 4. He committed ritual suicide 5. Richard Nixon 6. Burt Bacharach 7. The Social Democratic Party 8. Albert Finney 9. In an air accident 10. Aldo Moro 11. J.R. Tolkien 12. Bishop Abel Muzorewa 13. Italy 14. No reigning Japanese emperor had ever before left Japan 15. Lancelot Hogben

QUIZ 79
POT LUCK
1973

1 Where was Charles Lockwood captured in 1973?

2 Which part of the Skylab station was damaged and had to be repaired?

3 Who sang *Can the Can*?

4 Where was President Makarios re-elected?

5 Who topped the US charts with *My Love* in 1973?

6 Where did Fianna Fail fail in an election?

7 Which Rugby League team won the 1973 Challenge Cup Final?

8 Which Second Division soccer team won the FA Cup?

9 Which country had VAT for the first time in 1973?

10 Where did a government announce plans to save the tiger?

11 Which country took over the kingdom of Sikkim?

12 Where did President Lon Nol escape assassination?

13 On which island did Noel Coward die?

14 Which was Roger Moore's first Bond film?

15 In which 1973 film did Richard Dreyfuss play a "typical" US teenager?

ANSWERS

1, Argentina 2, Solar panels 3, Suzi Quatro 4, Cyprus 5, Paul McCartney and Wings 6, Republic of Ireland (General Election 1973) 7, St Helens 8, Sunderland 9, United Kingdom 10, India 11, India 12, Cambodia 13, Jamaica 14, *Live and Let Die* 15, *American Graffiti*

QUIZ 74
SPORT

1 Who was Liverpool's manager in 1971?

2 Who or what was Brigadier Gerard?

3 Who was Mr Lu?

4 Which sporting body had the initials BBBC?

5 How many matches did the rugby Lions lose on their 1971 tour down under?

6 Was the famous Gordon Brown of 1971 a rugby player or a Chancellor of the Exchequer?

7 Who won for the first time in England, after 39 years?

8 What did Ken Tyrrell design?

9 What was Peter Gethin's sport?

10 Which star striker was known as "Sniffer"?

11 Who rode a horse called Doublet to a gold medal?

12 In what event?

13 For whom did Ted Macdougall score nine times in November 1971?

14 Against whom?

15 And what was the score in the match?

ANSWERS

WORLD EVENTS
1970

1 Which French leader did Richard Nixon meet in 1970?

2 Which country's airline, El Al , was attacked by terrorists in West Germany?

3 Of which country was Mr Kosygin the prime minister?

4 Which president narrowly escaped assassination in 1970?

5 In which country was Milton Obote nationalising industries?

6 Where were two government ministers named in inquiries into arms smuggling?

7 What firsts did Ann Hays and Elizabeth Hoisington achieve in the USA?

8 Which spacecraft splashed down safely on April 17 1970 ?

9 Who won the Bannside by-election in Northern Ireland?

10 Where was Clifford Dupont sworn in as president?

11 Which British car was to cease production?

12 Which US actor was fined in Britain for possessing cannabis?

13 Where was general Sir John Freeland the senior army commander?

14 Which country signed a 20-year "friendship treaty" with the USSR?

15 In which US state did six black people die in racial violence in May 1970?

ANSWERS

1. Georges Pompidou 2. Israel 3. USSR 4. Makarios of Greece 5. Uganda 6. Republic of Ireland 7. First women army generals 8. Apollo 13 9. Ian Paisley 10. Rhodesia 11. The Morris Minor 12. Tony Curtis 13. Northern Ireland 14. Czechoslovakia 15. Georgia

QUIZ 76
SPORT

●●●

1 Which teams took part in the longest-ever FA Cup game?

2 How long had it lasted when the fifth replay finally ended 1-0?

3 And who won?

4 In which game did teams compete for the Gillette Cup?

5 Who won it for the second year running in 1971?

6 What did the initials PFA mean to footballers?

7 For which London club did Graeme Souness play soccer in 1971?

8 What was played at the Old Warson Country Club in 1971?

9 Who won?

10 What nationality was racing driver Ronnie Peterson?

11 In which sport did Edward Heath captain the British team?

12 What was unusual about a new squash court in Sheffield in 1971?

13 Which golf event reached its 50th year in 1971?

14 Who won (for only the second time)?

15 In which sport did Phil Read win honours?

●●●

ANSWERS

1, Alvechurch and Oxford City 2, 11 hours 3, Alvechurch 4, Cricket 5, Lancashire 6, Professional Footballers Association 7, Spurs 8, The Ryder Cup 9, The USA 10, Swedish 11, Yacht racing (Admiral's Cup) 12, It had a glass back wall 13, The Walker Cup 14, Great Britain 15, Motorcycle racing

QUIZ 77
PEOPLE

◀◀

1 Who was prime minister of Israel in 1970?

2 Which saxophonist released an album called *Captain Marvel*?

3 Did Henry Kissinger remain secretary of state when Richard Nixon resigned?

4 Which millionaire went to Southeast Asia in 1970 to try to ransom U.S. prisoners of war?

5 Busby Berkeley died in 1976. For what kind of films was he famous?

6 Who wrote *Sophie's Choice*, published in 1979?

7 What prize did Isaac Bashevis Singer win in 1978?

8 From which city did the Bay City Rollers come?

9 Of which country was Dr. Hastings Banda president?

10 Who played Edward in the 1975 ATV series *Edward the Seventh*?

11 In the London theatre in 1975, who starred in *A Little Night Music*?

12 What did Lynette Alice Fromme and Sara Jane Moore separately attempt in 1975?

13 Who crowned himself as emperor in central Africa in 1977?

14 Benjamin Britten died in 1976. With which English county was he associated?

15 Who wrote *The Greening of America*?

◀◀

ANSWERS

1. Mrs. Golda Meir 2. Stan Getz 3. He continued to serve under Gerald Ford 4. Ross Perot 5. Hollywood musicals 6. William Styron 7. The Nobel prize for literature 8. Edinburgh 9. Malawi 10. Timothy West 11. Hermione Gingold 12. To assassinate President Ford 13. Jean-Bédel Bokassa 14. Suffolk 15. Charles Reich

QUIZ 70
SCIENCE & TECHNOLOGY

1 What name was given to the new highway linking Zambia and Botswana?

2 Which Arctic mammal was to be conserved by international agreement in 1975?

3 What was special about the birth of Louise Brown in 1978?

4 Which was the last link of the Pan-American Highway to be completed?

5 Kobayashi-Berger-Milon was discovered in 1975. What is it?

6 Which company introduced the Walkman in 1979?

7 What new form of memory for computers came into commercial production in 1978?

8 In the late 70s the U.S. and the Soviet Union were developing CPBs. What were they?

9 ESRO was renamed ESA. What do the initials ESA stand for?

10 Which country built the Ariel satellites?

11 Kara, Kresta and Kynda were classes of Soviet warship. Which type of ship?

12 Archaeologists discovered six royal tombs at Shibarghan in 1979. In which country?

13 Which Cambridge physicist became well known for his work on black holes?

14 Voyager 2 was launched in 1977. Was it a manned spacecraft or an unmanned probe?

15 What made smaller cars more popular in the United States in the 70s?

ANSWERS

1, The BotZam Highway 2, The polar bear 3, She was the first "test-tube baby" 4, The Darien Highway in Panama 5, A comet 6, Sony 7, Bubble memories 8, Charged particle beams for destroying missiles 9, European Space Agency 10, The United Kingdom 11, Cruiser 12, Afghanistan 13, Stephen Hawking 14, An unmanned space probe 15, The rise in the price of petrol

QUIZ 79
ARTS & ENTERTAINMENT

•••

1 Which prematurely aged corporal recorded *Grandad* in 1971?

2 In which TV show did he use make up to age a few years?

3 Which ex-Beatle made a triple album called *All Things Must Pass*?

4 Which single gave him his first solo hit in 1971?

5 For whom was *Baby Jump* a 1970 follow-up hit?

6 Were did Dave and Ansil Collins hail from?

7 Can you name their 1970 hit?

8 How many times did Dawn say we should knock?

9 Was Dawn a solo performer or a group?

10 Complete the title *Chirpy, Chirpy* …?

11 But who sang it?

12 And which part of the British Isles were they from?

13 And what was their follow-up hit?

14 Who were getting it on in July 1971?

15 And from which album did their hit come?

•••

ANSWERS

1, Clive Dunn 2, *Dad's Army* 3, George Harrison 4, *My Sweet Lord* 5, Mungo Jerry 6, Jamaica 7, *Double Barrel* 8, Three (*Knock Three Times*) 9, A group 10, *Cheep Cheep* 11, Middle of the Road 12, Scotland 13, *Tweedle Dee Tweedle Dum* 14, T Rex 15, *Electric Warrior*

QUIZ 80
SPORT

@@@

1 Which snooker player blew in to win the 1972 world title?

2 For whom did Lawrence Rowe play cricket?

3 What first did he achieve with the bat in 1972?

4 Who humbled mighty Newcastle in the FA Cup?

5 In which league were they then playing?

6 Which step upward did they make the following season?

7 Who was Supermac, then idolised by Newcastle fans?

8 What European trophy came to Glasgow in 1972?

9 Won by?

10 In which European city did their fans leave a bad impression?

11 Who was the winning manager of this team?

12 In which sport did Gloucester beat Moseley?

13 Where did Scotland and Wales refuse to go and play rugby in 1972?

14 What accident forced Gordon Banks to quit football?

15 Which team upset Celtic to win the 1972 Scottish League Cup?

@@@

ANSWERS

1, Alex "Hurricane" Higgins 2, West Indies 3, He scored centuries in both innings of his debut match 4, Hereford United 5, Southern League 6, They joined the Fourth Division 7, Malcolm Macdonald 8, The Cupwinner's Cup 9, Rangers 10, Barcelona 11, Willie Waddell 12, Rugby Union 13, Dublin 14, A car accident had cost him the sight of an eye 15, Partick Thistle

QUIZ 81
PEOPLE

●●

1   Who directed the 1979 film *Apocalypse Now*?

2   What kind of sculpture was originated by Alexander Calder, who died in 1976?

3   Who wrote *Whatever Happened to Sex*?

4   In which country did South Moluccan terrorists seize a train in 1975?

5   Who seized power in Pakistan in 1977?

6   Which Greek composer was freed from prison in 1970?

7   Which Western movie veteran finally won an Oscar in 1970?

8   Was he known as Duke, Earl or the Little Guy?

9   Sir John Barbirolli died in 1970. Which orchestra did he conduct from 1943 to 1968?

10 Hercule Poirot and Miss Marple were creations of which author, who died in 1976?

11 Which pop group did Mick Taylor leave in 1975?

12 Richard J Daley was mayor of which city from 1955 to 1976?

13 Who became conductor of the Liverpool Philharmonic Orchestra in 1979?

14 Which pre-war British foreign secretary and later prime minister died in 1977?

15 What title did he bear at his death?

●●

ANSWERS

QUIZ 82
POT LUCK
1978

●●●

1 What did the Americans say they'd found in their Moscow embassy?

2 From which musical came the song *You're the One that I Want*?

3 Who played Sandy in this film?

4 With which politician did newspapers link Norman Scott?

5 Who or what was Shirley Heights?

6 In which European country was the president forced to resign in 1978?

7 Where did a gas tanker explosion kill 188 holidaymakers?

8 Which jailed leader celebrated his 60th birthday in 1978?

9 In which country were the 1978 Commonwealth Games held?

10 Which holy relic went on show in Italy?

11 Which Kenyan leader died this year?

12 In which film did Jamie Lee Curtis make her debut?

13 Who was this actress's father?

14 Who played Lex Luther?

15 And in which film?

●●●

ANSWERS

1, Bugs (listening devices) 2, Grease 3, Olivia Newton-John 4, Jeremy Thorpe 5, The 1978 Derby winner 6, Italy 7, Spain 8, Nelson Mandela 9, Canada 10, The Turin Shroud 11, Jomo Kenyatta 12, Halloween 13, Tony Curtis 14, Gene Hackman 15, Superman

QUIZ 89
SPORT

eeeeeeeeeeeeeeeeeeeeeeeeeeeeeeeeeeeeeeeeeeeeeeeeeee

1 Leeds were favourites to win the 1971–72 championship, but who pipped them?

2 Managed by?

3 Where were Derby when they heard the title was theirs?

4 What did Karl Schranz do better than most?

5 What was his nationality?

6 Why was he thrown out of the 1972 Winter Olympics?

7 In which event did Ard Schenk win three golds?

8 Was Roberto Duran a boxer or a jockey?

9 What did the initials WCT stand for in tennis?

10 Which millionaire controlled the WCT?

11 Why did Newcombe, Ashe, Laver and Rosewall all miss Wimbledon in 1972?

12 Who lost the 1972 Wimbledon men's final?

13 Who beat him?

14 Which Irish star left Old Trafford in 1973?

15 Which manager had brought him to the club?

eeeeeeeeeeeeeeeeeeeeeeeeeeeeeeeeeeeeeeeeeeeeeeeeeee

ANSWERS

1, Derby County 2, Brian Clough and Peter Taylor 3, Majorca (their season had ended, Leeds lost their last match) 4, Ski 5, Austrian 6, For having advertising contracts 7, Speed skating 8, A boxer 9, World Championship Tennis 10, Lamar Hunt 11, There was a dispute about fees paid to WCT players 12, Ilie Nastase 13, Stan Smith 14, George Best 15, Matt Busby

QUIZ 84
WORLD EVENTS
1970

👞👞👞👞👞👞👞👞👞👞👞👞👞👞👞👞👞👞👞👞👞👞👞👞👞👞👞👞👞👞👞👞

1 How old was Bertrand Russell at his death?

2 Where was the first nerve transplant performed?

3 Who was the leader of the PLO?

4 Which rebel British colony became a republic in 1970?

5 Whose daughter did "Anastasia" claim to be?

6 Which prince took his seat in the House of Lords?

7 How long did dogs have to stay in quarantine under new 1970 regulations?

8 What could 18-year-olds do in Britain for the first time?

9 Where was Phnom Penh?

10 In which city is the Bogside, so often in the 1970s news?

11 Which company was developing the RB-211 engine?

12 Where did general Ojukwu surrender?

13 Whose forces had defeated him?

14 To which political party did MP Will Owen belong?

15 With what offence was he charged in 1970?

👞👞👞👞👞👞👞👞👞👞👞👞👞👞👞👞👞👞👞👞👞👞👞👞👞👞👞👞👞👞👞👞

ANSWERS

1, 97 2, West Germany 3, Yasir Arafat 4, Rhodesia 5, Tsar Nicholas II 6, Charles 7, A year 8, Vote 9, Cambodia 10, Londonderry 11, Rolls Royce 12, Biafra 13, The federal Nigerian government 14, Labour 15, Passing secrets

QUIZ 85
PEOPLE

eeeeeeeeeeeeeeeeeeeeeeeeeeeeeeeeeeeeeeeeeeeeee

1 Who was president of the Philippines throughout the 70s?

2 Charles de Gaulle died in 1970. In 1940 he became leader of which movement?

3 Which German-born space scientist retired from NASA in 1972?

4 The author of novels featuring Perry Mason died in 1970. What was his name?

5 Which Nobel prize winner claimed that vitamin C could protect against the common cold?

6 Which famous opera singer gave her last performance in 1974 and died in 1977?

7 Who was elected leader of the Conservative Party in 1975?

8 What award was given to two Belfast women, Mairead Corrigan and Betty Williams?

9 Max Ernst died in 1976. Of which artistic movements was he a pioneer?

10 Dame Edith Evans gave her last stage performance in 1974. Was she then 66, 76, or 86?

11 Paul Getty was immensely rich when he died in 1976. What was the source of his wealth?

12 What office did Nelson Rockefeller hold before he became U.S. vice president in 1974?

13 The comedian Sid James died in 1976. In which country was he born?

14 Who directed the 1978 film *The Deer Hunter*?

15 Of which British orchestra was Rudolf Kempe principal conductor from 1970 to 1975?

eeeeeeeeeeeeeeeeeeeeeeeeeeeeeeeeeeeeeeeeeeeeee

ANSWERS

1, Ferdinand Marcos 2, The Free French 3, Wernher von Braun 4, Erle Stanley Gardner 5, Linus Pauling 6, Maria Callas 7, Margaret Thatcher 8, The 1976 Nobel prize for peace 9, Surrealism and Dadaism 10, 86 years old 11, Oil investments 12, Governor of New York 13, South Africa 14, Michel Cimino 15, The Royal Philharmonic Orchestra

QUIZ 86
WORLD EVENTS
1970

•••

1 Where was the England soccer captain falsely accused of theft?

2 Who was he?

3 What was he alleged to have stolen?

4 Where were the England team headed for?

5 Which event did journalist Seymour Hersh uncover?

6 Which journalistic award did he receive in Vietnam?

7 With what terrorist group was Ahmed Jibril linked?

8 Which British MP lost his seat at Belper?

9 Where was President Ongania overthrown?

10 Which rock opera was staged at the New York Met?

11 Which group performed it there?

12 A British prince gained a degree in history. Who was he?

13 From which university did he receive it?

14 Which former leader was expelled from the Czech Communist party?

15 Whose wife (Caroline) was killed in a car crash in June 1970?

•••

ANSWERS

1, Bogota, Colombia 2, Bobby Moore 3, A gold bracelet 4, Mexico 5, The My Lai Massacre in Vietnam 6, Pulitzer Prize 7, Popular Front for the Liberation of Palestine 8, George Brown 9, Argentina 10, *Tommy* 11, The Who 12, Prince Charles 13, Cambridge University 14, Alexander Dubcek 15, Jeremy Thorpe, Liberal leader

POT LUCK

1 In which continent did the Ogaden War take place?

2 Who lost it?

3 Who was world snooker champion in 1978?

4 Who played his first Test for England as a batsman?

5 In which English town was the sitcom *Fawlty Towers* supposedly set?

6 Which insurance company planned a new, hi-tech, London headquarters?

7 Who released an album called *The Kick Inside*?

8 Who was captain of Argentina's World Cup winning team?

9 What did Lucius do in 1978?

10 In which country were Peabody awards given to TV shows?

11 Which fictional family lived at Southfork?

12 Which member of this family was played by Larry Hagman?

13 What, allegedly, did he ban the cast from doing on set?

14 Which pop singer's widow was to feature in this family saga?

15 Eddie and Alex played with which US rock band?

ANSWERS

1. Africa 2. Somalia 3. Ray Reardon 4. David Gower 5. Torquay 6. Lloyd's of London 7. Kate Bush 8. Daniela Passarella 9. Won the Grand National 10. USA 11. The Ewings 12. JR Ewing 13. Smoking 14. Priscilla Presley (widow of Elvis) 15. Van Halen

QUIZ 88
ARTS &
ENTERTAINMENT

●●●

1 Who was still waiting, but reached the top in Britain anyway?

2 Who sang *Hey Girl Don't Bother Me* in 1971?

3 Were they American or British?

4 For whom might the singer of *Maggie May* have played soccer professionally?

5 Who was he?

6 Which group from Wolverhampton arrived on the pop scene in 1971?

7 Which was their first British number one?

8 Who was the fastest milkman in the West?

9 And who sang about him?

10 Who wanted to teach the world to sing in 1972?

11 How had this song begun its life?

12 Who were the group's two girl singers?

13 Which Eurovision song did they enter in 1972?

14 For whom was *Telegram Sam* a hit?

15 Complete the 1972 group name: Chicory ...?

●●●

ANSWERS

1. Diana Ross 2. The Tams 3. American 4. Brentford 5. Rod Stewart 6. Slade 7. Coz I Luv You 8. Ernie 9. Ernie 10. The New Seekers 11. As an advertising jingle (for a well known cola) 12. Eve Graham and Lyn Paul 13. Beg, Steal or Borrow 14. T Rex 15. Tip

QUIZ 89
PEOPLE

•••

1 Mao Tse-tung died in 1976. What did his Little Red Book contain?

2 Lily Pons died in 1976. Was she a ballet dancer, a singer, or an actress?

3 Sybil Thorndike died in 1976. Who was her husband from 1908 until his death in 1969?

4 Jean Renoir died in 1979. What was the name of his film about World War I?

5 The creator of *Little Grey Rabbit* died in 1976. What was her name?

6 Which of the Nobel prizes did Milton Friedman win in 1976?

7 Who wrote *The Boys from Brazil*, about clones of Adolf Hitler?

8 Who succeeded Lord Olivier in 1973 as director of the National Theatre?

9 For what achievements did Vaclav Havel originally become known?

10 Of which country was Sir Keith Holyoake prime minister and later governor-general?

11 In which year did Princess Margaret and Lord Snowdon announce their separation?

12 Who was elected mayor of New York in 1977?

13 Charlie Chaplin left the United States in 1952. Did he ever return?

14 Among his songs were *Hey Joe* and *Foxy Lady*. He died in 1970. Who was he?

15 Which political party did Vanessa Redgrave support in the 70s?

•••

ANSWERS

1, His thoughts and a summary of his speeches and writings 2, A singer 3, Lewis Casson 4, *La Grande Illusion* 5, Alison Uttley 6, The Nobel prize for economics 7, Ira Levin 8, Peter Hall 9, His plays, such as The Memorandum 10, New Zealand 11, 1976 12, Ed Koch 13, He returned in the 70s to receive an Academy Award 14, Jimi Hendrix 15, The Workers' Revolutionary Party

QUIZ 90
POT LUCK

🌸🌸🌸🌸🌸🌸🌸🌸🌸🌸🌸🌸🌸🌸🌸🌸🌸🌸🌸🌸🌸🌸🌸🌸🌸🌸🌸🌸🌸🌸🌸🌸

1. What year was the voting age in the United States lowered from 21 to 18?

2. In which country did General Zhia oust Prime Minister Bhutto in 1977?

3. The German director of the influential *Metropolis* died in 1976. Who was he?

4. Who held office for only 33 days in 1978?

5. 900 people died in a mass suicide in Guyana in 1978. Who led this bizarre cult?

6. What year was Britain's winter of discontent?

7. Which former World War II commander and member of Britain's royal family was murdered by the IRA in 1979?

8. In which country were 100 US embassy staff held hostage in 1979?

9. Which country invaded Afghanistan in 1979?

10. Who was the second husband of crime writer Agatha Christie, who died in 1976 still best known by her first husband's name?

11. On what were people in Britain asked to vote in a 1975 referendum?

12. Which art historian was outed as a Soviet spy in 1979?

13. What year was the Watergate burglary in Washington, D.C.?

14. Which Olympics were hit by terrorists who attacked Israeli athletes?

15. Who led the Iranian revolution of 1979?

🌸🌸🌸🌸🌸🌸🌸🌸🌸🌸🌸🌸🌸🌸🌸🌸🌸🌸🌸🌸🌸🌸🌸🌸🌸🌸🌸🌸🌸🌸🌸🌸

ANSWERS

1, 1971 2, Pakistan 3, Fritz Lang 4, Pope John Paul I 5, Rev. Jim Jones 6, 1978–79 7, Earl Mountbatten of Burma 8, Iran 9, The USSR 10, Sir Max Mallowan 11, Whether or not to stay in the EEC 12, Sir Anthony Blunt 13, 1972 14, Munich, 1972 15, Ayatollah Khomeini

QUIZ 91
SCIENCE & TECHNOLOGY

1 China began using pinyin for certain purposes in 1979. What is pinyin?

2 To which planet did the Soviet Union launch two spacecraft in 1971?

3 Architects began to include atriums in their designs in the late 70s. What are atriums?

4 What type of missile was the Soviet Galosh?

5 Which unmanned craft landed on Mars in 1976?

6 In the 70s several nations were harvesting krill in Antarctic seas. What is or are krill?

7 In which year was the Pompidou Centre opened in Paris?

8 When were the SALT I arms control agreements made?

9 Which Soviet nuclear icebreaker reached the North Pole in 1977?

10 What name did the BBC give to its Teletext services in the 70s?

11 Dennis Gabor won the Nobel prize for physics in 1977 for work in what technique?

12 Which Asian country exploded its first nuclear device in 1974?

13 The Tarbela Dam in Pakistan was completed in 1975. Which river does it dam?

14 The Trans-Alaska pipeline opened in 1977. To which southern port did the oil flow?

15 What disease affected people who attended an American Legion convention in 1976?

ANSWERS

1, A system for writing Chinese in the Roman alphabet 2, Mars 3, Glass-roofed indoor garden spaces 4, An ABM or antiballistic missile 5, Viking 1 and Viking 2 6, Shrimp-like crustaceans 7, 1977 8, In 1972 9, Arktika 10, Ceefax 11, Holography 12, India 13, Indus River 14, Valdez 15, Legionnaires disease

QUIZ 92
ARTS &
ENTERTAINMENT

‍‍‍

1 Who played Charles I in the film *Cromwell*?

2 Who played Cromwell?

3 Which teenager starred as Bobbie in *The Railway Children*?

4 Who played the station keeper Mr Perks?

5 And who directed this film?

6 In which 1970 film did Edward Fox and Julie Christie co-star?

7 Which assassin did Fox play in another film?

8 Who was he trying to kill in this role?

9 Were the characters played by Nanette Newman and Malcolm McDowell in *The Raging Moon* disabled or in jail?

10 Which Redgrave starred as *Mary Queen of Scots* on screen?

11 Whose tales were turrned into a ballet?

12 Name the squirrel character who lost his tail in the ballet.

13 Who played the young Churchill in 1972?

14 What was the film title?

15 Complete the 1971 title: *A Clockwork ...*?

‍‍‍

ANSWERS

QUIZ 99
WORLD EVENTS
1970

❦❦❦

1 In which country did Gomulka resign in 1970?

2 Where was *Pravda* published?

3 Which writer did this paper attack in print?

4 Which drug causing deformity in children was at the centre of lawsuits?

5 The death was announced of which British wartime commander in Burma?

6 Who said "We are all the President's men"?

7 Whose funeral took place at Colombey-les-Deux-Eglises?

8 Representing the Queen at the official ceremony for this person was whom?

9 In which church was the official ceremony and requiem mass held?

10 Gdansk was the scene of rioting in which country?

11 Which new government ministries were created in Britain in October?

12 Where did hundreds of people die in a typhoon?

13 Kenneth Baker was elected to represent which political party?

14 Who was named President of the United Arab Republic?

15 Which was the largest country within this group of nations?

❦❦❦

ANSWERS

1, Poland 2, USSR 3, Alexander Solzhenitsyn 4, Thalidomide 5, Viscount Slim 6, Henry Kissinger 7, De Gaulle 8, Prince Charles 9, Notre Dame Cathedral 10, Poland 11, Trade and Industry; Environment 12, The Philippines 13, The Conservative Party 14, Anwar Sadat 15, Egypt

QUIZ 94
SPORT

❦❦

1 Which golfer was nicknamed Super Mex?

2 Which cricket county won their first trophy ever in 1972?

3 Who was their captain that year?

4 What was his native county?

5 Which sporting side did John Pullin skipper in South Africa?

6 Which bank clerk from Perth bamboozled England?

7 Who was Grand Prix's youngest ever world champion in 1972?

8 Who quit as manager of Manchester City, handing over to Malcolm Allison?

9 In which game did the 4-tackle rule become the six-tackle rule?

10 What was Tom Weiskopf's sport?

11 In 1972, which US team lost an Olympic match for the first time since 1936?

12 Who beat them in the final?

13 Who almost fooled Marathon officials?

14 Which event cast a shadow over the 1972 Games?

15 What was Mark Spitz's longest event in the 1972 Olympic pool?

❦❦

ANSWERS

1, Lee Trevino 2, Leicestershire 3, Ray Illingworth 4, Yorkshire 5, England's rugby team 6, Australian bowler Bob Massie who took 16 wickets for 137 runs in a 1972 Test 7, Emerson Fittipaldi 8, Joe Mercer 9, Rugby League 10, Golf 11, The basketball team 12, The USSR 13, A student who ran out in front of the leading runners just outside the stadium 14, The shooting of Israeli athletes by Palestinian guerrillas 15, 200 metres (freestyle and butterfly)

QUIZ 95
ARTS & ENTERTAINMENT

1 Who wrote a play called *Stripwell* (1975)?

2 Who made a TV kids' show called *Potty Time*?

3 Who wrote a *Phallic Novel* in 1971?

4 Which US poet famous her her three-cornered hats died in 1972?

5 Which French actor starred in the film *State of Siege*?

6 Who made a film called *Days of Hope*?

7 Who wrote the music for a show about Jeeves?

8 Who wrote a novel about changing places?

9 In what art form did Maina Gielgud perform?

10 Which comedian made a breakthrough on *Tiswas*?

11 What did the show's title stand for?

12 Which 1970 show had Superstar in its title?

13 In what year did *Evita* appear?

14 Who was the real life Evita?

15 Was Edward Burra, who died in 1976, an artist or a writer?

ANSWERS

1, Howard Barker 2, Michael Bentine 3, Alberto Moravia 4, Marianne Moore 5, Yves Montand 6, Ken Loach 7, Andrew Lloyd Webber 8, David Lodge (Changing Places, 1975) 9, Ballet 10, Lennie Henry 11, This is Saturday, Wear A Smile 12, Jesus Christ Superstar 13, 1978 14, Eva Peron 15, An artist

POT LUCK

••

1 Which country's leader in 1970 was Edward Gierek?

2 James Callaghan lost his vote of confidence in 1979 by how many votes?

3 At what age could people in Britain vote after 1970?

4 Which tiny European state refused to allow women the vote in February 1971?

5 Which British politician was killed by an IRA bomb in the House of Commons car park in 1979?

6 Which European country legalized divorce in November 1970?

7 Which square in Paris was known as the Place de l'Etoile before 1970?

8 Where was the Ho Chi Minh Trail?

9 Which US university was the scene of a terrible 1970 shooting?

10 In which African country was the Biafran war, which ended in 1970?

11 What food commodity was in short supply in Britain in 1974: sugar, coffee or butter?

12 What year in the 70s was the first British soldier killed in Northern Ireland?

13 Who promoted himself general and made himself president of Uganda in 1971?

14 In which country was Roberto Levington toppled from power in 1971?

15 Thomas Dewey died in 1971: in which country had he been a prominent politcian?

••

ANSWERS

1, Poland 2, One 3, 18 4, Liechtenstein 5, Airey Neave 6, Italy 7, Place Charles De Gaulle 8, Vietnam 9, Kent State, Ohio 10, Nigeria 11, Sugar 12, 1971 (February) 13, Idi Amin 14, Argentina 15, The United States

QUIZ 97
WORLD EVENTS
1970

ccccccccccccccccccccccccccccccccccccccccccccccc

1 Where did Abdul Razak succeed Abdul Rahman?

2 Which airliner made its first landing at Heathrow?

3 On which magazine did George Gale succeed Nigel Lawson as editor?

4 Which Egyptian leader died of a heart attack?

5 Which Southeast Asian state declared itself a republic?

6 Where did a tidal wave kill thousands of people?

7 Who promised socialism within liberty as he was sworn in as president?

8 Where did Hafez al-Assad seize power?

9 What is the capital of that country?

10 Which European country's western frontier was the Oder-Neisse Line?

11 Who said that cardinals at 80 were too old to vote for popes?

12 Where was the FLQ organization active?

13 What happened to James Cross in Canada?

14 Who was prime minister of Canada at the time?

15 Which award did Norman Burlang win?

ccccccccccccccccccccccccccccccccccccccccccccccc

ANSWERS

1, Malaysia 2, Concorde 3, *The Economist* 4, Nasser 5, Cambodia 6, East Pakistan 7, Allende of Chile 8, Syria 9, Damascus 10, Poland's 11, The Pope 12, Quebec 13, He was kidnapped by Quebec separatists 14, Pierre Trudeau 15, Nobel Peace Prize

QUIZ 90
PEOPLE

1 Who won the Nobel prize for peace in 1979 for her work in Calcutta?

2 Gracie Fields died in 1979: on which Italian island?

3 Who released an album called *Journey Through the Secret Life of Plants*?

4 Which famous singer died in 1977 after playing a round of golf?

5 Sir Allen Lane died in 1970. Which famous company did he found?

6 Which British film actor received an Oscar posthumously in 1977?

7 Who became foreign minister of Israel after the 1977 election?

8 Who captained England's cricket team in the 1977 test series against Australia?

9 The novelist Nicholas Monsarrat died in 1979. What was his best known work?

10 Which army did Arnold Brown lead in 1977?

11 Can you name President Jimmy Carter's younger brother?

12 Erich Remarque died in 1970. What was his most famous novel?

13 The teacher accused in the "monkey trial" of 1925 died in 1970. What was the offence?

14 Of which country did Morarji Desai become prime minister in 1977?

15 In which year did Queen Elizabeth II celebrate her Silver Jubilee?

ANSWERS

1, Mother Teresa 2, Capri 3, Stevie Wonder 4, Bing Crosby 5, Penguin Books 6, Peter Finch 7, Moshe Dayan 8, Mike Brearley 9, The Cruel Sea 10, The Salvation Army 11, Billy Carter 12, All Quiet on the Western Front 13, Teaching the theory of evolution 14, India 15, 1977

QUIZ 99
SPORT

* *

1 Which country won 17 of 29 track and field gold medals at the 1972 Olympics?

2 Which event did Richard Meade win for Britain?

3 Which country did Teofilo Stevenson represent?

4 And in which sport?

5 Which gold did John Akii-Bua of Uganda win?

6 Which Finn won both 5000 and 10,000 metres?

7 Who was Australia's star of the pool in 72?

8 Who said "The medals weighed a lot"?

9 In which sport did Jonah Barrington win a 6th British Open title in 1973?

10 What was his native county?

11 Who almost scored three successive 100s in Tests for England v Pakistan?

12 Which World Cup winning England centre half called it a day in 1973?

13 What was his brother doing on the same day (28 April 1973)?

14 For whom did Phil Bennett play international rugby?

15 Which horse did Red Rum overtake to win the 1973 Grand National?

* *

ANSWERS

1, The USA 2, The individual three-day event 3, Cuba 4, Boxing 5, 400 metres hurdles 6, Lasse Viren 7, Shane Gould 8, Mark Spitz 9, Squash 10, Cornwall 11, Dennis Amiss (he scored 99 in the third knock) 12, Jack Charlton 13, Playing his last game for Manchester United 14, Wales 15, Crisp

1 Which church accounced it would ordain women ministers?

2 Whose election victory as prime minister in June was a surprise to most?

3 How many Liberal MPs were elected to the new parliament?

4 Which party had been portrayed as Yesterday's Men?

5 Which Labour veteran became a life peer aged 85?

6 Who became the new deputy leader of the Labour Party?

7 Where was Neil Blaney cleared of gun-running charges?

8 Which group of workers staged their first national strike since 1926?

9 Who went on trial in Los Angeles for the murder of actress Sharon Tate?

10 Where was Dawson's Field?

11 What happened there in September 1970?

12 What national airlines did the aircraft belong to?

13 Which woman was arrested while trying to hijack an aircraft over the UK?

14 What happened to her and other terrorist prisoners?

15 In which country did PLO activity provoke fierce response from king and army?

ANSWERS

1. The Methodist Church 2, Edward Heath's 3, Six 4, The Conservatives 5, Emmanuel Shinwell 6, Roy Jenkins 7, Dublin 8, The dockers 9, Charles Manson 10, Jordan 11, Three aircraft were hijacked and blown up 12, BOAC, Pan Am and Swissair 13, Leila Khaled 14, They were freed 15, Jordan

ARTS &
ENTERTAINMENT

●●●

1 Which actor knight got a peerage in 1970?

2 Who wrote *First Love, Last Rites*?

3 Who provided the music for the TV series *Elizabeth R*?

4 Who played Elizabeth?

5 Which role did Robert Hardy play in this series?

6 Which Denny joined Paul in Wings?

7 Which David was shut up in *Colditz* for a TV series?

8 In which series did he keep vanishing?

9 Which theatre group was founded by Frank Dunlop in 1970?

10 Which TV comedy series marched off screen in 1974?

11 Which Eric was in it?

12 Which Benny kept everybody (well, many people) laughing?

13 In which country, other than Britain, was he a smash?

14 With which art form was Michael Bogdanov associated?

15 Which British actor starred in *Death in Venice*?

●●●

ANSWERS

1, Laurence Olivier 2, Ian McEwan 3, David Munrow 4, Glenda Jackson 5, The Earl of Leicester 6, Denny Laine 7, David McCallum 8, *The Invisible Man* 9, The Young Vic 10, *Monty Python's Flying Circus* 11, Eric Idle 12, Benny Hill 13, The USA 14, Theatre 15, Dirk Bogarde

PEOPLE

●●

1 In which city was Patricia Hearst convicted of armed robbery in 1976?

2 Field Marshal Viscount Slim died in 1970. In which campaign had he found fame?

3 Merle Oberon died in 1979. Was she born in Australia, England, or the United States?

4 Naum Gabo died in 1977: was he an actor, an architect, or an artist?

5 Who succeeded Gough Whitlam as prime minister of Australia in 1975?

6 Christopher Ewart-Biggs was killed by terrorists in 1976. What position did he hold?

7 Saul Bellow won the Nobel prize for literature in 1976. Where was he born?

8 Who directed *Butch Cassidy and the Sundance Kid*?

9 Who wrote a series of novels called *A Dance to the Music of Time*, completed in 1975?

10 Of which country did Elias Sarkis become president in 1976: Egypt, Lebanon, or Syria?

11 What was unusual about the actors in the 1976 film *Bugsy Malone*?

12 What was the name of Paul McCartney's group in the mid-70s?

13 Who starred in the 1976 film *The Shootist*?

14 Which European dictator died in November 1975?

15 Who directed the 1970 film *Kes*?

●●

ANSWERS

1, San Francisco. 2, The Burma Campaign. 3, In Australia. 4, An artist. 5, Malcolm Fraser. 6, British ambassador to Ireland. 7, Canada. 8, George Roy Hill. 9, Anthony Powell. 10, Lebanon. 11, They were children. 12, Wings. 13, John Wayne. 14, General Franco. 15, Ken Loach

QUIZ 109
POT LUCK

eccecececececececececececececececececececececececececece

1 Which British daily newspaper closed down in March 1971?

2 Of which country was General Yakubu Gowon head of state?

3 Who became Argentina's president in 1973?

4 Which musical was made about his wife?

5 Of which country was Margrethe II queen?

6 Which country's prime minister was Gough Whitlam?

7 What year did East and West Germany join the United Nations?

8 Which European country was ruled by the generals in 1973?

9 Who was this country's exiled king?

10 Which island was led by Dom Mintoff?

11 Marshal Tito was leader of which European country?

12 What was his real name?

13 William Tolbert was president of which African state?

14 What is its capital city?

15 Named after who?

eccecececececececececececececececececececececececececece

ANSWERS

1, *The Daily Sketch* 2, Nigeria 3, Juan Peron 4, *Evita* 5, Denmark 6, Australia 7, 1973 8, Greece 9, Constantine 10, Malta 11, Yugoslavia 12, Josip Broz 13, Liberia 14, Monrovia 15, US President James Monroe (1758–1831)

QUIZ 104
SPORT

1 What was "Venkat's" full name?

2 And what did he do?

3 Who was America's new blond golf star of 1973?

4 Flemming Delfs won a world title for Denmark in 1977; in what?

5 Which Swede made his first start on Centre Court?

6 Who was Jan Webster?

7 Who said "we were outbatted, outbowled and outfielded"?

8 Who had beaten his side?

9 Who made nought in his only one-day international innings?

10 Who scored his 100th century in 1973?

11 What world record did David Bedford break in 1973?

12 Which sport staged its first women's world cup?

13 Who became England's most capped soccer player in 1973?

14 What total did he reach in June that year?

15 How many more caps did he win?

ANSWERS

1, Srinivasaraghavan Venkataraghavan 2, He was an Indian spin bowler 3, Johnny Miller 4, Badminton 5, Björn Borg 6, England's rugby scrum half in 1973 7, Ray Illingworth, England cricket captain 8, The West Indies 9, Gary Sobers 10, Colin Cowdrey 11, 10,000 metres 12, Cricket 13, Bobby Moore 14, 107 15, One

QUIZ 105
WORLD EVENTS
1971

1 Which organization was headed by Lord Fiske?

2 What did the letters OPEC stand for?

3 What did its members plan to do?

4 Which government minister's home was bombed by the Angry Brigade?

5 What did President Nixon warn to steer clear of Cuba?

6 Where was the Commonwealth Conference held in this year?

7 Who was the boss in Uganda?

8 Where were the Tupamaros guerrillas active?

9 Why were there no letters on doormats in January?

10 Into which country did Israeli troops move to attack terrorist bases?

11 From where were A-bombs banned by a treaty signed in Moscow?

12 Which British politician suggested that immigrants be repatriated?

13 Who promoted himself to the rank of general a month after taking power?

14 Britain agreed to sell seven of what to South Africa?

15 Which European state said 'no' to votes for women?

ANSWERS

1, The Decimal Currency Board 2, Organization of Petroleum Exporting Countries 3, Raise oil prices 4, Employment minister Robert Carr 5, Soviet submarines 6, Singapore 7, Idi Amin 8, Uruguay 9, Postal workers went on strike 10, Lebanon 11, The sea floor 12, Enoch Powell 13, Idi Amin 14, Helicopters 15, Liechtenstein

QUIZ 106
SPORT

●●●

1 Which team caused an upset in the 1973 FA Cup final?

2 Whom did they beat?

3 Against whom did Bobby Riggs play and lose?

4 Which team thwarted England's footballers with a 1-1 draw at Wembley?

5 Who had called their goalkeeper a clown?

6 What was the consequence of the drawn game?

7 From which post did Denis Follows retire in 1973?

8 Which Scotland manager resigned in 1973?

9 Which golf event was held for the first time in Scotland?

10 Which course staged the event?

11 Who won the 1973 500cc motorbike world title?

12 Who won the first indoor Davis Cup final in 1973?

13 Which managerial pair left Derby?

14 Who took over as manager?

15 Which club did the pair then move to?

●●●

ANSWERS

1, Sunderland 2, Leeds United 1-0 3, Billie Jean King 4, Poland 5, Brian Clough, on TV 6, England failed to progress to the World Cup finals 7, FA secretary 8, Tommy Docherty 9, The Ryder Cup 10, Muirfield 11, Phil Read 12, Australia 13, Brian Clough and Peter Taylor 14, Dave Mackay 15, Brighton

QUIZ 107
PEOPLE

ŒŒŒ

1 In 1976 Helmut Schmidt faced which other Helmut in the German federal election?

2 Elvis Presley died in 1977. What was his middle name?

3 King Carl XVI Gustaf married in 1976. Of which country is he king?

4 Who played Captain Hawkeye Pierce in *M.A.S.H.*?

5 Of which country was Jacobus J Fouche president in 1973?

6 Gordon Jackson won an Emmy award in 1976 for playing the butler in which TV series?

7 Which art historian was revealed in 1979 as having spied for the Soviet Union?

8 Who succeeded John Lynch in 1979 as prime minister of Ireland?

9 Which world-famous author was deported from the Soviet Union in 1974?

10 Do you know the first name of President Carter's wife?

11 Which two positions did Leonid Brezhnev hold in the U.S.S.R. from 1977?

12 Who became chairman of British Leyland in 1979?

13 Ernesto Geisel became president in 1974: of which country?

14 Of which country was Bruno Kreisky chancellor throughout the 70s?

15 Queen Elizabeth II toured the U.S. in July 1976. What was the occasion?

ŒŒŒ

ANSWERS

1, Helmut Kohl 2, Aron 3, Sweden 4, Alan Alda 5, South Africa 6, Upstairs, Downstairs 7, Anthony Blunt 8, Charles Haughey 9, Alexander Solzhenitsyn 10, Rosalynn 11, General secretary of the Communist party and president 12, Sir Michael Edwardes 13, Brazil 14, Austria 15, The bicentennial of the United States

QUIZ 108
SPORT

●●

1 Who lost his England job for World Cup failure?

2 Who took over as caretaker boss?

3 For whom did Colin Bell play club football?

4 What change came into force in English soccer in 1973–74?

5 Which Guyanese batting star bowed out of the West Indies side in 1974?

6 For which country did Rod Dixon run?

7 Where were the 1974 Commonwealth Games held?

8 Which country produced the Games' star, Filbert Bayi?

9 Who got his revenge on Joe Frazier?

10 What was Rudy Hartono's sport?

11 Which batsmen amassed 380 in two innings against New Zealand?

12 Had Australia and New Zealand played official Tests before 1974?

13 Which Reds found themselves dropping into Division Two?

14 Whose goal sent his former club down?

15 What colour were McLaren racing cars to be painted in a new deal?

●●

ANSWERS

1. Sir Alf Ramsey 2, Joe Mercer 3, Manchester City 4, Three up and three down (promotion and relegation) 5, Rohan Kanhai 6, New Zealand 7, Christchurch, New Zealand 8, Tanzania 9, Muhammad Ali 10, Badminton 11, Greg Chappell of Australia 12, No 13, Manchester United 14, Denis Law, playing for Manchester City 15, Red and white

QUIZ 109
ARTS & ENTERTAINMENT

1 Which Michael starred in *Sleuth* on the big screen?

2 Who was his co-star?

3 Who played Mahler for Ken Russell?

4 Who wrote *A Clockwork Orange*?

5 Who filmed it?

6 Who played Estella in a 70s film of *Great Expectations*?

7 Who played Pip in this film?

8 Who directed the film *Bugsy Malone*?

9 Which pop star appeared in *The Man Who Fell To Earth*?

10 Which Roger was being Tommy in a rock-opera

11 With whom did Glenda Jackson co-star in *A Touch of Class*?

12 Who played Superman?

13 Which fictional hero featured in *The Spy Who Loved Me*?

14 Who starred in *The Bitch*?

15 Who played the *Elephant Man*?

ANSWERS

1, Michael Caine 2, Laurence Olivier 3, Robert Powell 4, Anthony Burgess 5, Stanley Kubrick 6, Sarah Miles 7, Michael York 8, Alan Parker 9, David Bowie 10, Roger Daltry of the Who 11, George Segal 12, Christopher Reeve 13, James Bond 14, Joan Collins 15, John Hurt

QUIZ 110
POT LUCK

●●●

1 How many people were unemployed in Britain in 1971: 800,000, 1.8 million, or 3 million?

2 How many engines did the new TriStar and DC-10 airliners each have?

3 From where did *Luna 16* return in September 1970?

4 Which Pacific ex-colony became independent in 1970?

5 A British government minister in the 90s; in 1974 a guest on the *Morecambe and Wise* television show. Who is she?

6 Were members of OPEC concerned about the price of oil, oranges or olives?

7 Was Bishop Muzorewa a leading figure in: a) the Rhodesia crisis or b) the US Civil Rights movement?

8 In which country did Kerry Packer build a media empire?

9 Who said in 1974 ... "Those who hate you don't win unless you hate them"?

10 Who succeeded Richard Nixon as US President on 9 August 1974?

11 Which American politician hit three spectators with his first two shots in a 1971 Bob Hope Desert Classic?

12 By what name did Peter Sutcliffe become infamous?

13 Was the Awami League a political movement, a breakaway soccer league, or a 70s pop group?

14 Which British tennis star married Chris Evert?

15 Where were the world's first surviving sextuplets born in 1974?

●●●

ANSWERS

1, 800,000. 2, Three 3, The Moon 4, Fiji 5, Glenda Jackson 6, Oil 7, a) 8, Australia 9, Richard Nixon 10, Gerald R. Ford 11, Spiro Agnew 12, The Yorkshire Ripper 13, A political movement in what became Bangladesh 14, John Lloyd 15, South Africa

QUIZ 111
SPORT

••

1 What was Jeff Thomson's sport?

2 Which team did Willie-John McBride captain in South Africa?

3 Among the teams's stars were England winger David … who?

4 and Irish centre Mike …?

5 In what race did the leader wear a yellow jersey?

6 And who was the leader for the 5th time in 1974?

7 Was he French, Dutch or Belgian?

8 Which US tennis stars were romantically linked for a time?

9 Which old favourite did one of them beat in the 1974 Wimbledon final?

10 In which sport did Holland win the first women's world cup in 1974?

11 From whom did Ray Kennedy join Liverpool?

12 Who made the signing, then said he was resigning?

13 Which British runner broke the world 3000-metre record in 1974?

14 Where were the 1974 World Cup finals staged?

15 Which team played "total football"?

••

ANSWERS

1, Cricket 2, The British Lions rugby team 3, Duckham 4, Gibson 5, The Tour de France 6, Eddy Merckx 7, Belgian 8, Jimmy Connors and Chris Evert 9, Ken Rosewall 10, Hockey 11, Arsenal 12, Bill Shankly 13, Brendan Foster 14, West Germany 15, The Dutch

QUIZ 112
WORLD EVENTS
1971

●●

1 Which head of state requested a pay rise?

2 Who called this truly regal cheek?

3 What were Labour's views on EEC membership: yes or no?

4 Where were talks about Britain's entry to the EEC being held?

5 Which country needed help to feed Bangladeshi refugees?

6 What was the name of the new 'breakaway' wing of the IRA?

7 How much did the government want to charge for entry to museums?

8 Which political party regained control of the GLC?

9 What was the GLC?

10 What place in history had the *Daily Sketch* newspaper, closed this year?

11 Who or what were talked of as 'lame ducks'?

12 Which Scottish shipyard was the centre of heated discussions over its future?

13 Where was Tito re-elected as president?

14 With what issue were the 'Pentagon Papers' concerned?

15 What unusual vehicle did David Scott and James Irwin drive?

●●

ANSWERS

1. The Queen 2. Richard Crossman MP 3. No 4. Paris 5. India 6. The Provisionals 7. 10p–20p 8. Labour 9. The Greater London Council 10. Britain's oldest tabloid newspaper 11. Failing industries 12. Upper Clyde Shipbuilders 13. Yugoslavia 14. The Vietnam War 15. The Apollo 14, 'Moon buggy' or lunar rover

PEOPLE

1. What caused the death of Lord Mountbatten in 1979?

2. Of which country was Raymond Barre premier?

3. What triggered the second oil crisis of the 70s?

4. In the U.S., the first legal casino outside Nevada opened in 1979. In which city?

5. John Grierson died in 1972. For what kind of film-making was he famous?

6. Indira Gandhi lost an election in 1977. Which party did she lead?

7. Of which historical figure was the 1972 film *Lamb* a fictional biography?

8. Who came to the throne of Spain in 1975?

9. Gordon C. Liddy took part in a famous burglary. It became known by what name?

10. What nationality was 1973 EEC Commissioner Patrick Hillery?

11. To what post was William Whitelaw appointed in 1972?

12. Who directed the film version of *The Boy Friend*?

13. Hubert Humphrey died in 1978. What was his middle name?

14. Zulfikar Ali Bhutto won an election in 1977: in which country?

15. The author of *Lolita* died in 1977. What was his name?

ANSWERS

1. An IRA bomb in his fishing boat 2. France 3. The revolution in Iran 4. Atlantic City 5. Documentary films 6. The Congress Party of India 7. Lady Caroline Lamb 8. Prince Juan Carlos 9. Watergate 10. Irish 11. Secretary of state for Northern Ireland 12. Ken Russell 13. Horatio 14. Pakistan 15. Vladimir Nabokov

QUIZ 114
WORLD EVENTS
1971

1 Which prestige car company fell on hard times?

2 Which politician married Margaret Sinclair?

3 Against which legislation were British trade unionists agitating?

4 What damaged the Senate wing of the Capitol in Washington?

5 Which Southeast Asian countries had US troops invaded?

6 Where did Brian Faulkner become prime minister?

7 Who introduced VAT in his budget in the UK?

8 Where did premier Demiral resign?

9 Which Commonwealth nation was split by civil war?

10 Which part of this country broke away?

11 Who was leader of the breakaway state?

12 Who was found guilty of massacre in Vietnam?

13 UK unemployment was at which record high: a)800,000 b) 500,000 or c)1.5 million?

14 Which nation launched the *Soyuz 10* spacecraft?

15 Where did a dictator die and his 19-year-old son take over?

ANSWERS

1, Rolls Royce 2, Pierre Trudeau 3, The Industrial Relations Bill 4, A bomb 5, Laos 6, Northern Ireland 7, Anthony Barber 8, Turkey 9, Pakistan 10, East Pakistan 11, Sheikh Mujibur Rahman 12, Lt. William Caley 13, a) 14, USSR 15, Haiti

POT LUCK

1 Did the population of London rise or fall between 1961 and 1971?

2 What did the initials ZANU stand for in African politics?

3 What post did Sir Arthur Bliss hold from 1953 to 1975?

4 In which sport was Douglas Haston celebrated throughout the 70s?

5 Which US President did Prince Charles go to visit in July 1970?

6 Which British prime minister's wife became famous for her poems?

7 What year were the British people asked to vote whether or not to stay in the European Community?

8 David Bedford set a world record for track and field in 1973; at what distance?

9 What were first seen on British motorways in 1970?

10 What was Black Arrow?

11 What was its intended purpose?

12 What level did inflation reach in the UK in 1975: 10%, 15% or 25%?

13 For which English county was Salop the suggested official name in 1974 (but rejected)?

14 What moved to Nine Elms in London in 1974?

15 Which group of British workers sought a 47 per cent pay rise in 1971?

ANSWERS

1, It fell, from 7.9 million to just under 7.4 million 2, Zimbabwe African National Union 3, Master of the Queen's Music 4, Mountain climbing 5, Richard Nixon 6, Harold Wilson's wife Mary 7, 1975 8, 10,000 metres 9, Crash barriers 10, A rocket 11, To put a British satellite into space 12, 25% 13, Shropshire 14, The Covent Garden fruit and vegetable market 15, Miners

QUIZ 116
ARTS & ENTERTAINMENT

● ●

1 At which studios was *Star Wars* made?

2 Who played C3-PO?

3 Who played Richard Hannay in the 1978 version of *The Thirty Nine Steps*?

4 Who recorded an album called *Captain Fantastic*?

5 Who teamed up with Dave Stewart in 1977?

6 Who wrote *Pennies From Heaven*?

7 Who was the male star of this TV play?

8 Which TV quiz show sat people in a black chair?

9 Who said "I've started so I'll finish"?

10 Who played Tom Good on TV?

11 Who played his wife?

12 In which cartoons series were Fred and Barney still going strong?

13 In which TV show did Richard Beckinsale and Paula Wilcox co-star?

14 Who drove a bus for laughs?

15 In which show?

● ●

ANSWERS

1, Elstree 2, Anthony Daniels 3, Robert Powell 4, Elton John 5, Annie Lennox 6, Dennis Potter 7, Bob Hoskins 8, *Mastermind* 9, Magnus Magnusson 10, Richard Briers 11, Felicity Kendall 12, *The Flintstones* 13, *The Lovers* 14, Reg Varney 15, On the Buses

QUIZ 117
PEOPLE

1 What prize did Andrey Sakharov win in 1975?

2 The conductor Leopold Stokowski died in 1977. In which country was he born?

3 Who succeeded Cecil Day-Lewis as poet laureate?

4 Who played the male lead in *Last Tango in Paris*?

5 Who was born in Lubeck as Herbert Enst Karl Frahm?

6 To what post was Sir Martin Ryle appointed in 1972?

7 Which party in Canada was led by Rene Levesque?

8 For what office was Sargent Shriver a candidate in 1972?

9 Who succeeded Kenneth MacMillan as artistic director of the Royal Ballet?

10 Which much-loved jazz trumpeter died in 1971?

11 What position did Valery Giscard d'Estaing hold in 1977?

12 In which year were Princess Anne and Captain Mark Phillips married?

13 Who succeeded William Whitelaw as secretary of state for Northern Ireland?

14 In which show did Miss Piggy play a part?

15 Of which country did Mohammad Daud Khan become president in 1973?

ANSWERS

1, The Nobel prize for peace 2, England 3, Sir John Betjeman 4, Marlon Brando 5, Willy Brandt 6, Astronomer Royal 7, The PQ or Parti Qubecois 8, Vice president of the United States 9, Norman Morrice 10, Louis Armstrong 11, President of the French Republic 12, 1973 13, Francis Pym 14, *The Muppet Show* 15, Afghanistan

QUIZ 110
POT LUCK

●●

1 Natalia Makarova defected to the West from the USSR; was she a dancer, an athlete or a scientist?

2 In which country did Idi Amin become president in 1971?

3 Of which part of the United Kingdom was Brian Faulkner a prominent leader in the early 70s?

4 Which member of Britain's royal family died in Paris in 1972?

5 Who was convicted in 1971 for the murder of Sharon Tate and four others in Hollywood?

6 Who succeeded Harold Wilson as Britain's prime minister in 1976?

7 Who became Roman Catholic archbishop of Westminster in 1976?

8 Who left British politics in 1976 to become President of the EEC Commission?

9 Was Dame Janet Baker celebrated for her singing, cooking or scientific achievements?

10 What African country was led until 1971 by Milton Obote?

11 Where was the Bar-Lev Line, attacked in 1973?

12 Which party did Clement Freud represent when elected as an MP in 1973?

13 Whom did five Oxford colleges agree to accept for the first time in 1972?

14 Who was re-elected as US President in 1972?

15 Who was the defeated Democrat candidate in the 1972 US presidential election?

●●

ANSWERS

1, A dancer 2, Uganda 3, Northern Ireland 4, The Duke of Windsor 5, Charles Manson 6, James Callaghan 7, Basil Hume 8, Roy Jenkins 9, Singing 10, Uganda 11, The Sinai desert, between Egypt and Israel 12, Liberal Party 13, Women students 14, Richard Nixon 15, George McGovern

QUIZ 119
SCIENCE & TECHNOLOGY

1 The first U.S. space station was launched in 1973. What was its name?

2 Why was the temple of Isis at Philae in Egypt dismantled in 1976?

3 What sort of weapon was Poseidon?

4 Which volcano erupted on Guadeloupe in 1977?

5 In the 70s large quantities of which natural resource were discovered in Mexico?

6 With which country did Britain co-operate in building the Jaguar fighter?

7 In industrialized countries, did the birthrate rise or fall in the 70s?

8 What took place at Mururoa Atoll in July 1976?

9 What work did the Glomar Challenger undertake in the 70s?

10 What sort of weapon is the Abrams?

11 What was IDOE?

12 In 1976 economists celebrated the bicentennial of a famous book. What was its short title?

13 Which of these diseases was eradicated in the 70s: Lassa fever, smallpox, tuberculosis?

14 Telephone companies began to instal fibre-optic systems in the 70s. What sort of fibre?

15 The CT scan was developed in the 70s to examine which part of the human body?

ANSWERS

1. Skylab 2. To prevent it being flooded by the Aswan High Dam 3. A submarine-launched ballistic missile 4. La Soufrière 5. Petroleum (oil) 6. France 7. The birthrate fell 8. Two nuclear tests by France 9. Deep-sea drilling 10. A main battle tank 11. The International Decade of Ocean Exploration 12. The Wealth of Nations 13. Smallpox 14. Glass 15. The skull and brain

QUIZ 120
ARTS & ENTERTAINMENT

1 Which David commentated on the snooker on TV?

2 Who played a king with six wives?

3 What was the name of the series?

4 Complete the title: *Randall and …*?

5 Who starred in *For The Love of Ada*?

6 Who played *Catweazle*?

7 Who played *Kojak*?

8 Did he have a brother or a wife appearing in the same show?

9 Who played *Jason King* on TV?

10 Which TV detective did Peter Falk create as an actor?

11 In which TV series were Barlow and Watt to be found?

12 What kind of animal was *Skippy*?

13 What did Mike Yarwood do on TV that made him a star?

14 Which prime minister was he particularly fond of?

15 Who played *Budgie* on TV?

ANSWERS

1, David Vine 2, Keith Michell 3, *The Six Wives of Henry VIII* 4, Hopkirk (Deceased) 5, Wilfred Pickles and Irene Handl 6, Geoffrey Bayldon 7, Telly Savalas 8, A brother 9, Peter Wyngarde 10, *Columbo* 11 *Softly, Softly* 12, A kangaroo 13, He was an impressionist 14, Harold Wilson (he often did impressions of Wilson) 15, Adam Faith

QUIZ 121
WORLD EVENTS

✦✦

1 Who was Canada's prime minister from 1968 to1979?

2 Of which province did Rene Levesque become premier?

3 Which US President came from Plains, Georgia?

4 Which advanced naval craft had he helped to develop during his service career?

5 Whom did he succeed as president?

6 Who had to give way to Margaret Thatcher in 1975?

7 Which party did Gordon Wilson represent as an MP?

8 Which prime minister resigned unexpectedly in 1976?

9 Who succeeded him?

10 What job did this politician have before 'moving up'?

11 What is Ronald Reagan's middle name?

12 When did Reagan first run for president?

13 Of which state was he governor in the 1970s?

14 What former US attorney-general was freed from prison in 1979?

15 Whom did Walter Mondale serve as vice-president?

✦✦

ANSWERS

1, Pierre Trudeau 2, Quebec 3, Jimmy Carter 4, Nuclear submarines 5, Gerald Ford 6, Edward Heath 7, Scottish Nationalists 8, Harold Wilson 9, James Callaghan 10, Foreign Secretary 11, Wilson 12, 1968 13, California 14, John Mitchell 15, Jimmy Carter

SPORT

1 Who scored the fastest goal in a World Cup final (1974)?

2 Playing for which team?

3 But who won the match, and the trophy?

4 Which were Britain's only representatives in the World Cup finals?

5 Where was the "rumble in the jungle"?

6 Who fought whom?

7 Which promoter put on the contest?

8 For whom did Gordon Greenidge score a debut century?

9 Who retired as manager of Spurs in 1974?

10 Whom did Spurs appoint to take over?

11 What nationality was Joao Havelange?

12 Which world governing body did he lead from 1974?

13 Who rode to new success on Yamaha?

14 What was Hugo Porta's sport?

15 For which country?

ANSWERS

1, Johann Neeskens 2, Holland 3, West Germany 4, Scotland 5, Kinshasa 6, Mahammed Ali fought and beat George Foreman 7, Don King 8, West Indies 9, Bill Nicholson 10, Terry Neill 11, Brazilian 12, FIFA 13, Giacomo Agostini (7th successive 350 cc world title) 14, Rugby union 15, Argentina

QUIZ 129
ARTS & ENTERTAINMENT

1 In which series did Roger Moore and Tony Curtis co-star?

2 Who starred as Joe in *Room At The Top* on TV?

3 Which series about the sea and ships hauled in viewers?

4 What was the name of the ship that featured in the series?

5 Which Ronnies came together for laughs?

6 Which Michael began his TV chat shows?

7 Who starred as *Edna the Inebriate Woman*?

8 Complete this TV title: *Mission …*?

9 Was *Alias Smith and Jones* a crime series or a Western?

10 Who were the stars?

11 Which character in *Coronation Street* electrocuted herself?

12 Who first presented *The Generation Game*?

13 And who gave us *Sale of the Century*?

14 What business were the *Brothers* in?

15 Who played Lord Peter Wimsey in 1972?

ANSWERS

1. *The Persuaders* 2, Kenneth Haigh 3, *The Onedin Line* 4, The Charlotte Rhodes 5, Corbett and Barker 6, Michael Parkinson 7, Patricia Hayes 8, *Impossible* 9, A Western 10, Ben Murphy and Pete Duel 11, Valerie Barlow 12, Bruce Forsyth 13, Nicholas Parsons 14, Road haulage 15, Ian Carmichael

QUIZ 124
POT LUCK

●●

1 What were the first names of President Nixon's two daughters?

2 What award did Henry Kissinger accept in 1973 for the Vietnam War ceasefire?

3 Which famous Soviet scientist won worldwide admiration and the 1975 Nobel peace prize for promoting peace?

4 Which two Middle Eastern leaders shared the 1978 Nobel Peace prize?

5 Which country did Haille Selassie lead until being deposed in 1974?

6 Where did John Marshall succeed Keith Holyoake as prime minister in 1972?

7 Where did Birendra become king in 1972?

8 What post did Joseph Luns of the Netherlands accept in 1971?

9 What was Colonel Rudolf Abel who died in Moscow in 1971 known to be?

10 What British government post did David Owen take on in 1977?

11 What office did Dean Acheson (died 1971) hold in the US government?

12 The designer of a famous quality car died in 1971: who was he?

13 What nationality was diplomat Ralph Bunche, who died in 1971?

14 Chester Conklin (died 1971) was a famous a) boxer b) screen comedian or c) newspaper owner?

15 In which sport was Bobby Jones (died 1971) a legend?

●●

ANSWERS

1. Julie and Patricia 2. Nobel peace prize 3. Andrei Sakharov 4. Menachem Begin of Israel and Anwar el-Sadat of Egypt 5. Ethiopia 6. New Zealand 7. Nepal 8. Secretary-General of NATO 9. A spy 10. Foreign Secretary 11. He was Secretary of State 1949-53 12. W O Bentley 13. American 14. b) 15. Golf

WORLD EVENTS

NIXON PRESIDENCY

1 Who said "the title of peacemaker was the greatest honour history can bestow"?

2 Which country did US troops invade in 1970?

3 On which capital city did Nixon order bombing to be stepped up in 1972?

4 The US boosted sales of which farm product to the USSR?

5 What was Safeguard, proposed by Nixon?

6 Whom did Nixon defeat in the 1972 election?

7 Which ballroom dances did the Nixons favour at the White House?

8 Which musical instrument did Nixon play?

9 In what year was the Vietnam War ended?

10 Who became vie-president in 1973?

11 What name did Nixon suggest for his domestic programme?

12 Which country did Nixon visit in May 1982?

13 What change in voting age took place in 1970?

14 Which agency did Nixon set up in 1970 to tackle pollution?

15 What was Nixon granted by President Ford on September 8, 1974?

ANSWERS

1. Richard Nixon 2. Cambodia 3. Hanoi 4. Wheat 5. An antiballistic missile system 6. George McGovern 7. Waltzes and foxtrots 8. The piano 9. 1973 10. Gerald Ford 11. New Federalism 12. USSR 13. It was lowered to 18 14. The Environment Protection Agency 15. A pardon for all federal crimes he may have committed while President

PEOPLE

1 Andrey Gromyko served for many years in which post in the Soviet government?

2 In which country was the oil magnate Armand Hammer born?

3 In 1973 Helmut Kohl was elected chairman of which political party?

4 At which festival did Maharaj Ji arrive in a white Rolls Royce in 1971?

5 Which orchestra did Sir Georg Solti conduct in London?

6 Who played the lead in the 1972 film *Pope Joan*?

7 Who succeeded Roy Fuller in 1973 as professor of poetry at Oxford?

8 Which novelist of the Australian outback won the Nobel prize for literature?

9 Fulgencio Batista died in 1973. Which country did he once rule?

10 David Ben-Gurion died in 1973. Which political party did he found?

11 Who succeeded Jack Lynch in 1973 as prime minister of Ireland?

12 When W H Auden returned to England, where did he settle?

13 What was the speciality of the artist Christo in the 70s?

14 Whom did Bobby Fischer beat to become world champion chess player in 1972?

15 In which country was Henry Kissinger born?

ANSWERS

1, Foreign minister 2, The United States 3, The Christian Democratic Union or CDU 4, Glastonbury 5, Orchestra of the Royal Opera House 6, Liv Ullmann 7, John Wain 8, Patrick White 9, Cuba 10, The Palestine Labour Party, Mapai 11, Liam Cosgrave 12, Oxford 13, Immense outdoor wrappings and curtains 14, Boris Spassky 15, Germany

QUIZ 127
SPORT

●●●

1 Where did Ron Greenwood take a back seat?

2 Who refused to play South Africa in the Davis Cup final?

3 Who arrived at Elland Road for a brief stay?

4 What race took place at Watkins Glen?

5 What first did Mike Burton achieve in 1975?

6 Against whom was he playing?

7 Which tennis player headed west for the good life?

8 In which sport did Gustavo Thoeni of Italy win prizes?

9 Which British driver won his first GP in 1975?

10 Who were English Second Division champions in 1975?

11 Who was Aston Villa's manager when they won the 1975 League Cup?

12 Who were Australia's demon duo of fast bowling?

13 Which Scot found himself in the England hot seat?

14 Which team had Dickie Guy in goal and caused an FA Cup shock?

15 What league were this team then (1975)?

●●●

ANSWERS

1, West Ham. 2, India 3, Brian Clough (manager of Leeds for 44 days) 4, The US Grand Prix (1974) 5, First England rugby player to be sent off in an international 6, Australia 7, Martina Navratilova 8, Skiing 9, James Hunt 10, Manchester United 11, Ron Saunders 12, Lillee and Thomson 13, Mike Denness, captain of England's cricket team" 14, Wimbledon (who beat Burnley 1-0) 15, Southern League

QUIZ 120
WORLD EVENTS
WATERGATE

✏✏✏

1 In which city was the Watergate building?

2 What had its offices there?

3 How many Watergate 'burglars' were arrested?

4 Which of them was the 'security coordinator' for a pro-Republican committee?

5 What did the letters CRP stand for?

6 Which newspaper led the investigation into the Watergate incident?

7 Who were the journalists chiefly involved?

8 Who in April 1973 declared he'd had no part in Watergate?

9 Complete the name: G Gordon ...?

10 Who was first appointed special prosecutor to investigate?

11 Which former Presidential Counsel became a leading witness?

12 Who became the second special prosecutor?

13 From which post did Elliot Richardson resign?

14 Which former holder of the same post was convicted of criminal charges?

15 Which two Nixon aides were also found guilty in 1975?

✏✏✏

ANSWERS

1, Washington 2, The Democratic National Committee 3, Five 4, James W McCord Jnr 5, Committee for the Re-election of the President 6, *The Washington Post* 7, Carl Bernstein and Bob Woodward 8, President Nixon 9, Liddy 10, Archibald Cox 11, John Dean 12, Leon Jaworski 13, Attorney General 14, John Mitchell 15, John Erlichman and H R Haldeman

QUIZ 129
ARTS & ENTERTAINMENT

1 In which serial did Annie Sugden feature as a character?
2 What year did this show start?
3 Who played the nasty Nazi in *Colditz*?
4 And who played the comparatively nice one?
5 Who said "shut that door"?
6 Who played Van Der Valk?
7 What nationality was this character?
8 And what was his job?
9 Which sitcom raised race issues?
10 Who presented a series about America?
11 Who wandered into *The World of Beachcomber*?
12 Which Russell started chatting?
13 Who played Hawkeye in *M.A.S.H.*?
14 And what was Hotlips's surname?
15 Who played her in the series?

ANSWERS

1, *Emmerdale Farm* 2, 1972 3, Anthony Valentine 4, Bernard Hepton 5, Larry Grayson 6, Barry Foster 7, Dutch 8, A detective 9, *Love Thy Neighbour* 10, Alistair Cooke 11, Spike Milligan 12, Russell Harty 13 Alan Alda 14, Houlihan 15, Loretta Swit

QUIZ 130
PEOPLE

●●

1 Which party did Georges Marchais lead?

2 Which film actor, who died in 1973, played the lead role in *The Cruel Sea*?

3 What part did Liza Minnelli play in *Cabaret*?

4 Of which country was Mokhtar Ould Daddah the president?

5 What post was Elliot Richardson given in April 1973 in Richard Nixon's cabinet?

6 Who was principal conductor of the London Symphony Orchestra in the early 70s?

7 He directed *The Grapes of Wrath* and *The Quiet Man*. He died in 1973. Who was he?

8 Of which country was Alfredo Stroessner president in the 70s?

9 Which U.S. organization was headed for a time by L Patrick Gray III?

10 The musician Pablo Casals died in 1973. What was his instrument?

11 Who succeeded Eamon de Valera as president of Ireland?

12 Did he write *The Riddle of the Sands*?

13 In which country did Mariano Rumor become prime minister in 1973?

14 Pearl Buck died in 1973. What was her most famous book about China?

15 Pablo Picasso died in 1973. In which Spanish city was he born?

●●

ANSWERS

1, The French Communist Party 2, Jack Hawkins 3, Sally Bowles 4, Mauritania 5, Attorney general 6, Andre Previn 7, John Ford 8, Paraguay 9, The FBI 10, The cello 11, Erskine Childers 12, No, the author was his father, also called Erskine Childers 13, Italy 14, *The Good Earth* 15, Malaga

QUIZ 131
POT LUCK

●●●

1 Of which country was Sean Lemass (died 1971) a former leader?

2 Who became famous for mysteriously bending spoons?

3 A government minister who died in 1974 left some controversial Diaries. Who was he?

4 Famous for his clock-hanging sequence and other silent film comic-heroics, he died in 1971; who was he?

5 Which South African golfer won his third British Open title in 1974?

6 Which England football manager resigned in 1977 to go to the United Arab Emirates?

7 Of which club side was he manager before becoming England boss?

8 A French actor, known for his suave style and tilted straw hats, died in 1974. Name?

9 Which famous musical duke died in 1974?

10 This President of the United States took over from Franklin D Roosevelt; he died in 1972. Who was he?

11 Which writer was expelled from the USSR?

12 One of the greats of film-making, a little man with a moustache, cane, and a funny walk. He died in 1977; who was he?

13 In 1971 Fischer beat Petrosian – playing what?

14 In what artistic field was Sir Tyrone Guthrie (died 1971) famed?

15 Lord Avon died in 1977; by what name was he better known?

●●●

ANSWERS

1. The Irish Republic 2. Uri Geller 3. Richard Crossman 4. Harold Lloyd 5. Gary Player 6. Don Revie 7. Leeds United 8. Maurice Chevalier 9. Bandleader Duke Ellington 10. Harry S Truman 11. Alexander Solzhenitsyn 12. Charlie Chaplin 13. Chess 14. Theatre (as director) 15. Anthony Eden

QUIZ 192
SPORT

1 Which Barry was polishing up the track on two wheels?

2 Who became Sir Gary?

3 For whom did Franz Beckenbauer play in the 1975 European Cup final?

4 Which British team did they beat?

5 Which lads were on strike in 1975?

6 Who won the men's hockey world cup?

7 For what sport was the Nations Cup a new event?

8 Who beat Connors in an epic Wimbledon final?

9 Which number nine scored five for England?

10 Who played centre half in England's 1975 side under Don Revie?

11 Who fell out with the England boss?

12 Who won the "thriller in Manila"?

13 Which Niki was steering Ferrari to victory?

14 Which grey-haired batsman steadied England's cricketers?

15 For which county did he play?

ANSWERS

1, Barry Sheene 2, Gary Sobers 3, Bayern Munich 4, Leeds, 2-0 5, Stable lads 6, India 7, Tennis 8, Arthur Ashe 9, Malcolm Macdonald 10, Dave Watson 11, Kevin Keegan 12, Ali beat Frazier 13, Niki Lauda 14, David Steele 15, Northamptonshire

QUIZ 139
WORLD EVENTS
1971

••

1 Which London landmark was damaged by a bomb?

2 Which Rhodesian city was then called Salisbury?

3 Which two Asian countries went to war?

4 Which bar in Belfast was hit by a bomb in December 1971?

5 Where was the Plain of Jars?

6 Which troops captured it in 1971?

7 Where did Giovanni Leone become president?

8 How many ballots were needed to elect him?

9 Who was the new Secretary General of the UN?

10 What was his nationality?

11 The government of which island asked Britain to pay more for its bases there?

12 What was Britain's reaction to this?

13 Where did 162 people die in an hotel fire on Christmas Day 1971?

14 Which company had its Libyan assets nationalised? ·

15 Who had her 'pay' doubled?

••

ANSWERS

1, The Post Office Tower 2, Harare 3, India and Pakistan 4, McGuirk's 5, Laos 6, North Vietnamese 7, Italy 8, 22 9, Kurt Waldheim 10, Austrian 11, Malta 12, It withdrew its forces 13, Seoul, South Korea 14, BP 15, The Queen

QUIZ 134
SPORT

1 Who won what at Laurel Valley in 1975?

2 Which brother took over the Australian cricket captaincy in 1975?

3 What was John Stracey's missing initial?

4 And what was his sport?

5 Which cricketing footballer helped Leicestershire win the county championship?

6 For which club did Mick Channon play?

7 Which tennis star was dating Cliff Richard, according to the press?

8 Which title did she win in 1976, the first Briton to do so since 1966?

9 Which soccer team was managed by Lawrie McMenemy?

10 Whom did they beat in the 1976 Cup Final?

11 Who was Bill Shankly's successor as Liverpool manager?

12 Which little and larghe were his striking partnership?

13 Which Liverpool player became known as "Super-Sub"?

14 What sport did Ray Floyd play?

15 Who was "Merve the Swerve"?

•••

ANSWERS

1. The USA won the Ryder Cup 2, Greg Chappell, from Ian 3, H 4, Boxing 5, Chris Balderstone 6, Southampton 7, Sue Barker 8, The French Open 9, Southampton 10, Manchester United 11, Bob Paisley 12, Keegan and Toshack 13, David Fairclough 14, Golf 15, Welsh rugby star Mervyn Davies

PEOPLE

1975

●●

1 Who was the first to run a mile in under 3 min 50 sec?

2 Who became an urban guerrilla after being kidnapped by them?

3 Who sued the BBC over allegations of Mafia connections?

4 Where was Seamus McCusker shot dead?

5 What was the profession of Professor Fairley, killed by a London car bomb?

6 Which award went to Andrei Sakharov?

7 Which weapons had he helped to develop?

8 Where was Rachid Karami prime minister?

9 Who kidnapped Dutch businessman Tiede Herrema?

10 What job did Merlyn Rees hold in 1975?

11 Which brothers swapped the captaincy of Australia's cricket team in 1975?

12 Which emperor died in August?

13 Which Middlesex bowler took five wickets on his Test debut?

14 In whose name was a cricket pitch dug up and walls daubed with graffiti?

15 Who commanded the joint Apollo Soyuz space mission?

●●

ANSWERS

1, John Walker (New Zealand) 2, Patti Hearst 3, Frank Sinatra 4, Belfast 5, He was a cancer specialist 6, Nobel Peace Prize 7, The H-bomb 8, Lebanon 9, The IRA 10, Northern Ireland Secretary 11, The Chappells. Greg took over from Ian 12, Haile Selassie of Ethiopia 13, Phil Edmonds 14, George Davis 15, Tom Stafford and Aleksei Leonov

SCIENCE & TECHNOLOGY

1 Which U.S. nuclear power station suffered a serious accident in 1979?

2 What name was shared by the Soviet space stations of the 70s?

3 What was the name of the first U.S. space shuttle?

4 Which planet did *Venera 9* and *Venera 10* investigate in 1976?

5 The sinking of the *Amoco Cadiz* caused an oil pollution disaster on which coast?

6 *Pioneer 11* sent back data about Lapetus, Rhea and Titan. What are they?

7 Which science was made popular on television by Sir Mortimer Wheeler?

8 What did the HEAO or 'Einstein Observatory' satellites study?

9 What was unusual about the launch of Czechoslovakia's first satellite in 1978?

10 What did CITES set out to regulate?

11 When Skylab re-entered the atmosphere, on which country did wreckage fall?

12 Which company marketed a car called the Rabbit in the United States?

13 Which country developed oilfields called Frigg and Ekofisk?

14 What did Panama take over in 1979?

15 When two jumbo jets collided in 1977, 582 people died. Where did it happen?

ANSWERS

1. Three Mile Island 2. Salyut 3. *Enterprise* 4. Venus 5. Brittany, France 6. Moons of Saturn 7. Archaeology 8. X-ray sources in space 9. *Magion 1* was launched piggyback with a Soviet satellite 10. International trade in endangered species 11. Australia 12. Volkswagen 13. Norway 14. The Panama Canal Zone (but not the canal itself) 15. At Tenerife in the Canary Islands

QUIZ 137
ARTS &
ENTERTAINMENT

1 Who played Frank Spencer?

2 And who played his wife Betty?

3 What was the name of the comedy show?

4 In which show did Compo, Clegg and company feature?

5 Who said "I'm free"?

6 And in what show?

7 And what character did Mollie Sugden play in it?

8 What were the *Likely Lads* first names?

9 And who played them?

10 Which character was married to Thelma?

11 With which show did Esther Rantzen become associated?

12 Who played the matriarch in *The Brothers*?

13 Who played Robin Tripp?

14 In which series?

15 Which American became a star doing Kung Fu?

ANSWERS

1. Michael Crawford 2. Michelle Dotrice 3. *Some Mothers Do 'Ave 'Em* 4. *Last Of The Summer Wine* 5. John Inman 6. *Are You Being Served* 7. Mrs Slocombe 8. Bob and Terry 9. Rodney Bewes and James Bolam 10. Bob 11. *That's Life* 12. Jean Anderson 13. Richard O'Sullivan 14. *Man About The House* 15 David Carradine

QUIZ 130
POT LUCK

1   To whom did George Foreman lose the big fight of 1974?

2   For what was John McVicar notorious in Britain in 1970?

3   Salford's most famous painter died in 1976; who was he?

4   The man recognized as the father of the BBC died in 1971. Who was he?

5   Which formidable dame of the stage exited in 1976?

6   Which composer known for his work with the singer Peter Pears died in 1976?

7   What nationality was the comedian Fernandel, who died in 1971?

8   Which once-divine Asian head of state visited Britain in 1971?

9   The wife of one of the Allied leaders in World War II died in 1977; who was she?

10 Which England footballer left Liverpool for Hamburg in 1977?

11 One of the most famous opera stars of her time died in 1977; who was she?

12 Who did Mrs Thatcher appoint as her first Chancellor of the Exchequer in 1979?

13 A very English actress known for her funny monologues and revue work died in 1979; who was she?

14 Bessie Braddock who died in 1970 was a British MP; associated with which city?

15 Which orchestra conductor, internationally known for his work with the Hallé Orchestra, died in 1970?

ANSWERS

1, Muhammad Ali 2, Escaping from prison 3, L S Lowry 4, Lord Reith 5, Edith Evans 6, Benjamin Britten 7, French 8, Emperor Hirohito of Japan 9, Lady Spencer Churchill (widow of Sir Winston Churchill) 10, Kevin Keegan 11, Maria Callas 12, Geoffrey Howe 13, Joyce Grenfell 14, Liverpool 15, Sir John Barbirolli

QUIZ 139
SPORT

✻✻✻

1 Who was "Sevvy"?

2 Which carmaker launched a six-wheeled GP car in 1976?

3 Why did African countries boycott the 1976 Olympics?

4 Which New Zealander then won the 1500 m gold medal?

5 Who retained his 5000 and 10,000 metres titles?

6 Which event did Don Quarrie win?

7 Who was the star 400 m hurdler of his generation?

8 What sport was dominated by Kornelia Ender?

9 Where was she from?

10 Who got a perfect score in gymnastics?

11 How many medals did she win in 1976?

12 Who won Britain's first swimming gold medal since 1908?

13 In which event?

14 In which other event did Britain win gold in 1976?

15 Whose goals for Scotland beat England in 1976?

✻✻✻

ANSWERS

1, Severiano Ballesteros 2, Tyrrell 3, In protest at a New Zealand rugby tour of South Africa 4, John Walker 5, Lasse Viren 6, 200 metres 7, Ed Moses 8, Swimming 9, East Germany 10, Nadia Comaneci 11, 3 golds, 1 silver, 1 bronze 12, David Wilkie 13, 200m breaststroke 14, Modern pentathlon 15, Don Masson and Kenny Dalglish

QUIZ 140
WORLD EVENTS
1971

1. Which Chinese leader died in an air crash?
2. For what did 356 MPs vote yes and 244 vote no?
3. Which country's government said it was fighting, but did not know if it was at war?
4. Against whom were its troops engaged?
5. Who was Britain's Foreign Secretary at this time?
6. Where in Africa was he trying to negotiate a legal independence?
7. Where did 300 orphans die in a bomb attack?
8. What prize did Willy Brandt receive in Stockholm?
9. Who took over as Pakistan's president in December 1971?
10. Which country expelled many Iranians?
11. Where was Steve Biko opposing repression?
12. Whose defeated army was led by General Tiger Niqzi?
13. And whose army was led by Lt-General Aurora?
14. Who were 'razakars'?
15. Which side lost most casualties in the India-Pakistan war?

ANSWERS

1. Lin Piao, 2. Membership of the EEC, 3. Pakistan, 4. India, 5. Alec Douglas-Home, 6. Rhodesia, 7. Dacca, 8. Nobel Peace Prize, 9. Zulfikar Ali-Bhutto, 10. Iraq, 11. South Africa, 12. Pakistan (in the war with India), 13. India's, 14. East Pakistanis who fought for the Pakistan government, 15. Pakistan

PEOPLE

1972

1 Where did Gough Whitlam become prime minister?

2 What game was Bobby Fischer playing?

3 Who celebrated 25 years of royal wedded life?

4 What prize did Heinrich Boll receive?

5 What organization did the Rev 'Tubby' Clayton (died 1972) found?

6 What game did Victor Barna play?

7 Daisy Ashford died in 1972; what was her best-known book?

8 How old was she when she wrote it?

9 Where was Chiang Kai-shek president?

10 Who won all four major golf titles in 1972?

11 Who commanded Apollo 16?

12 Who was Mahalia Jackson, who died in 1972?

13 Which presenter of radio's *Any Questions* died?

14 What did Uffa Fox design?

15 George Sanders died in 1972; where was he born?

ANSWERS

1, Australia 2, Chess 3, The Queen and the Duke of Edinburgh 4, Nobel Prize for Literature 5, Toc H 6, Table tennis 7, *The Young Visiters* 8, Nine 9, Republic of China (Taiwan) 10, Jack Nicklaus 11, John Young 12, American gospel singer 13, Freddie Grisewood 14, Boats (yachts) 15, St Petersburg

QUIZ 142
WORLD EVENTS
1971

1 Where did a 1971 coup last only four days?

2 What did the IRA threaten to bomb?

3 With which of its neighbours did Syria break off relations?

4 What name did Egypt abandon in September 1971?

5 Which London bank lost half a million pounds to tunnel thieves?

6 Which jazzman played his first concert in the USSR?

7 What were demonstrators in Turkey fighting to stop?

8 Who arrived in Rome from self-imposed exile in Budapest?

9 In what year had this person taken refuge in the US embassy?

10 Where did the new Kennedy Arts Center open?

11 Which Gulf emirate became independent in August 1971?

12 In which city was the Crumlin Road prison?

13 With which organization was Joe Cahill linked?

14 For which country's refugees did Ravi Shankar and George Harrison play a charity concert in New York?

15 Which coins ceased to be legal tender in the UK?

ANSWERS

1, Sudan 2, The British mainland 3, Jordan 4, The United Arab Republic 5, Lloyd's
6, Duke Ellington 7, A new second airport 8, Cardinal Mindszenty 9, 1956
10, Washington 11, Bahrain 12, Belfast 13, The IRA 14, Bangladesh's 15, Old
pennies and threepenny bits

QUIZ 149
POT LUCK

ꞏꞏꞏ

1 Of which country was Pierre Trudeau prime minister during the 70s?

2 Egypt's president died in 1970. Who was he?

3 Which famous Frenchman died in November 1970?

4 Which famous British racing driver died in 1975?

5 Which country was ruled by Papa Doc Duvalier?

6 Bebe Daniels died in 1971; what was the name of husband and showbiz partner?

7 What was Gypsy Rose Lee (died 1970) famous for?

8 This leader once took off his shoe to bang the rostrum at the UN; he died in 1971. Who was he?

9 Whose lordly disappearance in 1974 sparked a man-hunt?

10 Why were the police seeking this person?

11 What year did Margaret Thatcher become leader of the Conservative Party in the UK?

12 Which royal duke and uncle to Queen Elizabeth II died in 1974?

13 Whose *Morning Cloud* sank in the English Channel?

14 With which British organization were Vic Feather and Len Murray connected?

15 Which singer died on the golf course in 1977?

ꞏꞏꞏ

ANSWERS

15, Bing Crosby
13, Edward Heath (it was his racing yacht) 14, The Trades Union Congress
murdering his child's nanny in London 11, 1975 12, The Duke of Gloucester
7, Stripping 8, Nikita Khruschev 9, Lord Lucan 10, He was suspected of
1, Canada 2, Nasser 3, Charles De Gaulle 4, Graham Hill 5, Haiti 6, Ben Lyon

QUIZ 144
ARTS &
ENTERTAINMENT

1 What did 'Two and Two make' in a play's title?

2 Another play title: John, Paul, George. Ringo and…who?

3 Who had a hit as Norman in *The Norman Conquests*?

4 Who wrote this play?

5 Complete the TV title: *A Man Called …*?

6 Who played the wheelchair detective?

7 And what was the name of his female assistant?

8 Who was *Barnaby Jones* on TV?

9 Which violinist wrote a memoir called *Unfinished Journey*?

10 Which "bird" family was a hit in the US?

11 And which pop star made his name in the show?

12 What was the name of the hamster who starred in a children's TV show?

13 What was Lauritz Melchior who died in 1973 famous as?

14 Which Italian actor starred in the film *City of Women*?

15 *Wheeltappers and … Club*? (Fill in the missing word of this TV show)

ANSWERS

15, *Shunters*
11, David Cassidy 12, Hammy 13, Opera singer 14, Marcello Mastroianni
7, Eve Whitfield 8, Buddy Ebsen 9, Yehudi Menuhin 10, *The Partridge Family*
1, Sex 2, Bert 3, Tom Courtenay 4, Alan Ayckbourne 5, *Ironside* 6, Raymond Burr

PEOPLE
ALL DIED IN 1972

•••

1 Who was Maurice Chevalier?

2 In which sport was Jo Bonnier a star?

3 Who was Peter Churchill?

4 He presented *Gardeners' Question Time* and *Down Your Way* on BBC radio. Who was he?

5 He found Australopithecus in East Africa. What was his name?

6 What did Sir Compton Mackenzie do?

7 Which oil millionaire, noted for flamboyance, died this year?

8 Who was the first boss of the FBI?

9 Who was Lord Parker?

10 Of which country was Lester Pearson the leader?

11 Which famous Russian-born aircraft-designer died this year?

12 With which industry was J Arthur Rank associated?

13 How did Prince William of Gloucester die?

14 What did the S in Harry S Truman stand for?

15 What nationality was Paul-Henri Spaak?

•••

ANSWERS

1. French singer and actor, 2. Motor racing 3. British secret agent during World War II 4. Franklin Engelmann 5. Louis Leakey 6. Wrote (he was an author) 7. Nubar Gulbenkian 8. J Edgar Hoover 9. A judge (Lord Chief Justice, 1958-71) 10. Canada (1963-68) 11. Igor Sikorsky 12. British film industry 13. In an aircraft crash 14. Nothing 15. Belgian

QUIZ 146
POT LUCK
ALL DIED IN 1973

●●

1 He made *Stagecoach* and many other Westerns, and died in 1973. Who was he?

2 Veronica Lake who died in 1973 was a famous: a) model b) singer or c) film actress?

3 For what was John Cranko (died 1973) famous?

4 He starred in *The Cruel Sea* and died in 1973; who was he?

5 For what was David Lack (died 1973) best known?

6 She wrote *Love in a Cold Climate* and died in 1973; her name?

7 Star of horror films, son of a famous father; died 1973. Name?

8 What instrument did jazzman Tubby Hayes (died 1973) play?

9 Louis Saint Laurent, who died in 1973, led which Commonwealth country?

10 Who was the Flying Finn, a runner who died in 1973?

11 Wilfred Rhodes, who died in 1973, was a famous sportsman: a) cricketer b) soccer player or c) tennis star?

12 A pin up famous for her legs, this movie star died in 1973. Who was she?

13 This film star who died in 1973 had an ugly mug but a winning smile, even as a gangster. Who was he?

14 An Italian actress, star of *The Rose Tattoo*, died 1973. Her name?

15 Britain's inventor of radar, he died in 1973. Who was he?

●●

ANSWERS

1, John Ford 2, c) 3, Ballet dancer 4, Jack Hawkins 5, He was a naturalist 6, Nancy Mitford 7, Lon Chaney Jr 8, Saxophone 9, Canada 10, Paavo Nurmi 11, a) 12, Betty Grable 13, Edward G Robinson 14, Anna Magnani 15, Robert Watson-Watt

QUIZ 147
SCIENCE & TECHNOLOGY

1 What was the mission of the Seasat satellite?

2 An educational research paper had the title Fifteen Thousand Hours. Why?

3 In 1977 astronomers detected the presence of rings around which planet?

4 What sort of vehicle was a Lunokhod?

5 Which great suspension bridge was under construction in England as the 70s ended?

6 Which was the first country to generate electricity from the sun for its national grid?

7 The Arlberg Tunnel was completed in 1978. In which country?

8 What happened to *Ekofisk Bravo 14* in April 1977?

9 Where did *Voyager 1* and *Voyager 2* observe active volcanoes in 1979?

10 What type of vessel was *Alvin*?

11 GARP began gathering data in 1978. What do the initials stand for?

12 Two cosmonauts spent 175 days in space in 1979: in which space station?

13 Which country tested its nuclear weapons at a site called Lop Nor?

14 Kohoutek was in the news in 1973. What is Kohoutek?

15 LASH is a patented way of shipping introduced in the 70s. What does LASH mean?

ANSWERS

1, Studying the world's oceans 2, The title referred to the time that most British children spend at school 3, Uranus 4, Lunokhods were Soviet unmanned lunar rovers 5, The Humber Bridge 6, France, in 1977 7, Austria 8, A blowout discharged 20,000 tons of oil into the North Sea 9, On Io, a satellite of Jupiter 10, A deep-sea submersible 11, Global Atmospheric Research Programme 12, Salyut 6 13, China 14, A comet 15, Lighter aboard ship or barge-carrying ship

QUIZ 148
ARTS &
ENTERTAINMENT

Complete the names and titles

1 DJ Pete …?

2 Racing commentator Peter …?

3 *Waggoner's* …? (radio soap)

4 *Sing Something* …? (radio)

5 Knotty …? (beloved of Ken Dodd)

6 Eric and …?

7 Russell … (chat show host)?

8 Les …? (comic)

9 *Upstairs, …?* (TV series)

10 *The Duchess of …?* (TV series)

11 *A Bouquet of …?* (TV series)

12 *Rich Man, …?* (TV series)

13 Chris … of *TISWAS*?

14 Jimmy … of *Top of the Pops*?

15 Norman … of *The Fosters* (TV)?

ANSWERS

QUIZ 149
WORLD EVENTS
1971

1 Where did prisoners hold 33 people hostage?

2 How many prisoners died in the shoot-out?

3 Did any hostages die?

4 Which former Soviet leader died in September 1971?

5 Which British motorway suffered serious fog-related crashes?

6 Why did people have no daily newspapers for four days?

7 Which country expelled 105 Soviet diplomats as spies?

8 Which Asian head of state visited Britain in October 1971?

9 How many times had he been abroad before?

10 Where was Soviet leader Kosygin attacked while on a visit?

11 What blew up in Glasgow, killing 20 people?

12 Which island said goodbye to the Royal Navy?

13 Which state was voted out of the UN?

14 Had such an event ever happened before?

15 Which state took its place?

ANSWERS

1, Attica Prison, New York 2, 32 3, Yes, 10 4, Khrushchev 5, The M6 6, Fleet Street was on strike 7, Britain 8, Emperor Hirohito of Japan 9, Never, as emperor 10, Canada 11, A gas main 12, Singapore 13, Taiwan 14, No 15, China

QUIZ 150
SPORT

ʚʚ

1 Who won the 1976 GP drivers' championship?

2 Which car was he driving?

3 Which county cricket team did Mike Brearley lead?

4 What was new in League soccer for offenders about to depart?

5 What game did Don January play?

6 What title did Geoff Hunt win for the first time in 1976?

7 For whom did Javed Miandad score a century on his debut?

8 Who said "We will make them grovel"?

9 Of whom was he speaking?

10 Who won the series?

11 And who was their best batsman, averaging over 118?

12 Who captained the West Indies to success?

13 What did Leighton Rees throw for Wales?

14 For whom did Brian Little score the winning goal in a League Cup marathon in 1977?

15 Whom did they beat?

ʚʚ

ANSWERS

1, James Hunt 2, McLaren 3, Middlesex 4, The red card 5, Golf 6, World Open squash championship 7, Pakistan 8, Tony Greig 9, The West Indies cricket team, about to tour England 10, West Indies 11, Viv Richards 12, Clive Lloyd 13, Darts 14, Aston Villa 15, Everton, after 330 minutes play

QUIZ 151
ARTS & ENTERTAINMENT

1 In which TV show did Karl Malden and Michael Douglas co-star?

2 Who was TV's *Police Woman*?

3 How many *Charlie's Angels* were there?

4 Who played Hutch in *Starsky and Hutch*?

5 Who wrote *A Bouquet of Barbed Wire*?

6 Who played Louisa Trotter?

7 And in which series?

8 Which series did Jean Marsh and Eileen Atkins create?

9 Before which war was it set?

10 And what position did Hudson occupy?

11 What was the cook's name?

12 Who played Ross in *Poldark*?

13 And who played Demelza?

14 Who played a character called Jack Ford?

15 In which TV series?

ANSWERS

1, *The Streets of San Francisco* 2, Angie Dickinson 3, Three 4, David Soul 5, Andrea Newman 6, Gemma Jones 7, *The Duchess of Duke Street* 8, *Upstairs, Downstairs* 9, World War I 10, Butler 11, Mrs Bridges 12, Robin Ellis 13, Angharad Rees 14, James Bolam 15, *When The Boat Comes In*

QUIZ 152
POT LUCK

ooooooooooooooooooooooooooooooooooooooooooooo

1   From which party did Lord George-Brown resign in 1976?

2   Who was the royal commander of HMS Bronington?

3   Which wartime commander, known to soldiers as Monty, died in 1976?

4   Which royal couple agreed to part in 1976?

5   She starred in many films as a dotty English lady, played *Miss Marple*, and died in 1971. Who was she?

6   In what sphere did Otto Klemperer win fame?

7   Abebe Bikila (died 1973) was famous as … what?

8   Was Bobby Darin (died 1973) a singer, a politician, or a baseball star?

9   What instrument did Pablo Casals play?

10 For what was Kenneth Allsop best known?

11 Was Kid Ory (died 1973) a jazz musician or a boxer?

12 This Chilean writer was for a time ambassador to France; he died in 1973. Name?

13 In which war did Eddie Rickenbacker, who died in 1973, become a hero?

14 Which one-eyed goalkeeper retired in 1973?

15 For which country did Sidney Barnes (died 1973) play cricket?

ooooooooooooooooooooooooooooooooooooooooooooo

ANSWERS

1, The Labour Party 2, The Prince of Wales 3, Field Marshal Viscount Montgomery 4, Princess Margaret and Lord Snowdon 5, Margaret Rutherford 6, Orchestral conductor 7, An athlete, Ethiopia's first international running star 8, A singer 9, Cello 10, His TV broadcasts and journalism 11, A jazz musician 12, Pablo Neruda 13, World War I (as a US air ace) 14, Gordon Banks (he had lost the sight of one eye in 1972 in a car crash) 15, Australia

WORLD EVENTS

1971

●●

1 Which part of Canada did the Queen tour in May 1971?

2 Where did the *Mariner 8* spacecraft end up?

3 Where was its target?

4 Which two Churches formed the United Reformed Church?

5 Which mountain foiled climbers Dougal Haston and Don Whillans?

6 Which country launched *Mars 2* and *Mars 3*?

7 Which disease killed many Bangladeshi refugees?

8 In which spacecraft were all three passengers found dead on landing?

9 Which country lifted its trade ban with China?

10 Who made a parachute jump into the Channel?

11 Where did the then worst-ever air disaster occur?

12 With what did an airliner collide?

13 Where was internment a matter of contention?

14 Which member of the royal family was 21 in 1971?

15 Where did General Banzer replace General Torres?

●●

ANSWERS

1, British Columbia 2, In the Atlantic Ocean 3, Mars 4, Presbyterians and Congregationalists 5, Mount Everest 6, The USSR 7, Cholera 8, Soyuz 11 9, The USA 10, Prince Charles 11, Japan 12, A Japanese air force fighter 13, Northern Ireland 14, Princess Anne 15, Bolivia

QUIZ 154
PEOPLE
JIMMY CARTER

●●

1 In what year was Carter elected US president?

2 Which party did he represent?

3 Which was his home state?

4 What are his full names?

5 Which armed service did he join?

6 Who in 1973, when told by Jimmy Carter that he was running for president, asked: "President of what?"

7 Which crop formed the family's main business?

8 Whom did Carter have as his running mate?

9 Which sitting president did Carter defeat?

10 Which missiles did Carter boost development of?

11 What did Carter ask his entire Cabinet to do in 1979?

12 Which canal was the subject of a treaty signed by Carter?

13 Which two countries did he try to bring together in the Camp David Agreement?

14 Where were US hostages held captive in 1979?

15 What is the name of the Carters' daughter?

●●

ANSWERS

1, 1976 2, Democrats 3, Georgia 4, James Earl Carter 5, US Navy 6, His mother Lillian 7, Peanuts 8, Walter Mondale 9, Gerald Ford 10, Cruise missiles 11, Resign 12, Panama Canal 13, Israel and Egypt 14, Iran 15, Amy

QUIZ 155
SPORT

●●●

1 Which England team goalkeeper joined Nottingham Forest?

2 Which French car maker returned to Formula One in 1977?

3 Why were Les Bleus happy at the end of the 1977 rugby season?

4 Which French rugby player was easily picked out by his flowing fair hair?

5 For whom did Steve Heighway play soccer?

6 Which sport celebrated a centenary of international play in 1977?

7 Where was the special centenary match played?

8 Who won?

9 Why was this a coincidence?

10 Which England batsman scored a gallant 174?

11 Which horse won his third Grand National in 1977?

12 Who was its trainer?

13 Where did the horse train?

14 How many times had it finished in the first two in the Grand National?

15 Which British boxer had his world title taken away from him?

●●●

ANSWERS

1, Peter Shilton. 2, Renault. 3, France won the Grand Slam. 4, Jean-Pierre Rives 5, Liverpool. 6, Cricket. 7, Melbourne. 8, Australia beat England. 9, Australia won the first ever Test in 1877, by the same margin of 45 runs. 10, Derek Randall 11, Red Rum. 12, Ginger McCain. 13, Southport beach. 14, Five (3 wins and 2 seconds). 15, John Conteh

QUIZ 156
WORLD EVENTS
1971

1 Where were three ships wrecked in January?

2 Which British sports body celebrated its centenary?

3 Which European country ruled Mozambique?

4 Where is Toscana, hit by earthquakes in January 1971?

5 Which US city suffered an earthquake in February 1971?

6 What was special about 15 February in Britain?

7 What stuffed animal was sold at Sotheby's for £900?

8 Where did William McMahon become prime minister?

9 On which island did student unrest lead to a national emergency?

10 Off which city was offshore oil discovered in India?

11 The Concert for Bangladesh in New York, was organised by which former Beatle?

12 This West African Commonwealth state became a republic. What was it?

13 On which mountain did an Indian climber die of cold?

14 Where did a court rule that aborigines did not own tribal lands?

15 After being dismantled and reassembled in Lake Havasu City, London Bridge spanned which American river?

ANSWERS

1. In the Channel, off Folkestone 2. The Rugby Football Union 3. Portugal 4. Italy 5. Los Angeles 6. Decimal currency was introduced 7. A great auk 8. Australia 9. Ceylon (Sri Lanka) 10. Bombay 11. George Harrison 12. Sierra Leone 13. Everest 14. Australia 15. Colorado River

QUIZ 157
ARTS &
ENTERTAINMENT

1 In which series on TV did Susan Hampshire play Lady Glencora?
2 Who starred as *Edward VII* on TV?
3 By what name did his wife appear in a hit TV comedy series?
4 And what was her real name?
5 Who played a cop named Jack Regan?
6 In which series?
7 Who was his co-star?
8 Which actress starred in *South Riding*?
9 Which queen did Annette Crosbie portray in 1975?
10 And whose wife did she play in the 90s?
11 Who lived next door to the Leadbetters?
12 In which series did HMS *Hero* feature?
13 In which series did Rigsby meet Miss Jones?
14 Which actor played him?
15 And which actress played her?

ANSWERS

1, *The Pallisers* 2, Timothy West 3, Sybil Fawlty 4, Prunella Scales 5, John Thaw 6, *The Sweeney* 7, Dennis Waterman 8, Dorothy Tutin 9, Victoria (in *Edward the Seventh*) 10, Victor Meldrew's in *One Foot in The Grave* 11, The Goods 12, *Warship* 13, *Rising Damp* 14, Leonard Rossiter 15, Frances de la Tour

QUIZ 158
PEOPLE
RICHARD NIXON

1 In which year was Nixon elected president of the USA?

2 Which Asian superpower did he visit in 1972?

3 Who was Nixon's first Vice-President?

4 Which of Nixon's sons-in-law was related to an ex-President?

5 What was the familiar first name of Mrs Nixon?

6 How had she got this name?

7 What did the M in Richard M Nixon stand for?

8 Who was Nixon's first Secretary of State?

9 Who was his second, and chief foreign affairs advisor?

10 How many children did the Nixons have?

11 In which US state was Nixon born, and buried?

12 What year did the Watergate burglary take place?

13 What did Nixon refuse to hand over to the House Judiciary Committee in 1973?

14 What year did Nixon resign?

15 Who succeeded him?

ANSWERS

1, 1968 2, China 3, Spiro Agnew 4, Julie Eisenhower's husband, David (grandson of former president Eisenhower) 5, Pat 6, She was born on St Patrick's Day 7, Milhous 8, William P Rogers 9, Henry Kissinger 10, Two 11, California 12, 1972 13, The Watergate tapes 14, 1974 15, Gerald Ford

QUIZ 159
POT LUCK

● ●

1 Which member of the British royal family was killed in a flying accident in 1971?

2 Which government announced in January 1971 that long hair was not illegal?

3 Was the terrorist group that bombed the British Home Secretary's home in 1971: a) Black September b) The Angry Brigade or c) The IRA?

4 Which Australian businesman took over London Weekend Television in 1971?

5 Which new tax was announced by the British government in 1971 as a replacement for purchase tax?

6 Why did footwear become higher in the early 70s?

7 Which member of the British royal family evaded a kidnap attempt in 1974?

8 On which London street did the kidnap attempt take place?

9 What kind of ration coupons were issued in Britain during 1973?

10 Which public holiday became official in the UK in 1978?

11 How did a Bulgarian defector named Georgi Markov meet his death in London in 1978?

12 Who had a hit with *Pretty Vacant?*

13 In which sporting event were 23 boats either sunk or abandoned?

14 Which horse won the 200th Derby, run in 1979?

15 Where did old London Bridge, replaced in 1973, end up?

● ●

ANSWERS

1, Prince William of Gloucester 2, The Soviet 3, b) 4, Rupert Murdoch 5, VAT (value added tax) 6, Platform heels became fashionable 7, Princess Anne 8, The Mall 9, Petrol coupons 10, May Day 11, He was allegedly murdered by an assassin using an umbrella-tip poison syringe 12, The Sex Pistols 13, The 1979 Fastnet yacht race 14, Troy 15, Lake Havasu City, in Arizona

QUIZ 160
SPORT

🍀🍀🍀🍀🍀🍀🍀🍀🍀🍀🍀🍀🍀🍀🍀🍀🍀🍀🍀🍀🍀🍀🍀🍀🍀🍀🍀🍀🍀🍀🍀🍀

1 Which sport had moved into the Crucible?

2 Where is the Crucible?

3 Who was the first world champion to win his title there, in 1977?

4 In which overseas venue had he last won the title, in 1970?

5 Which tennis player became known as "Superbrat"?

6 What was tennis star Gerulaitis's first name?

7 Who won the European Cup in 1977?

8 Were they already League champions?

9 Who had beaten them in the FA Cup final?

10 Who scored United's goals in a 2-1 win?

11 Which Tommy was the "iron man" of the Liverpool defence?

12 Was Lou Macari a Scottish or Italian international?

13 Which soccer manager quit soon after winning the Cup?

14 Who was picked to replace him?

15 What game did Tom Watson play better than most?

🍀🍀🍀🍀🍀🍀🍀🍀🍀🍀🍀🍀🍀🍀🍀🍀🍀🍀🍀🍀🍀🍀🍀🍀🍀🍀🍀🍀🍀🍀🍀🍀

ANSWERS

1, Snooker 2, Sheffield 3, John Spencer 4, Sydney 5, John McEnroe 6, Vitas
7, Liverpool 8, Yes 9, Manchester United 10, Stuart Pearson and Jimmy Greenhoff
11, Smith 12, Scottish 13, Tommy Docherty, from Manchester United 14, Dave
Sexton 15, Golf

QUIZ 161
WORLD EVENTS
1972

1 Who captured a Syrian general by mistake?

2 Where did this happen?

3 Who was Ulrike Meinhof?

4 To which group did she belong?

5 Where did the former King Edward VIII lie in state?

6 In which central African country did 400 miners die in a pit disaster?

7 Who chose Thomas Eagleton to run with?

8 Why was Eagleton's role short-lived?

9 Who said he had met IRA leaders in secret?

10 Whose brother-in-law was Sargent Shriver?

11 Who declared his intention to expel 50,000 people with British passports?

12 Which country was told to stick to a 50-mile fishing limit?

13 Which US governor was shot and wounded?

14 Which former Archbishop of Canterbury died in 1972?

15 To where did West Germany open an air link for the first time?

ANSWERS

1, Israeli troops 2, In Lebanon, during a raid 3, A German terrorist 4, The Red Army Faction 5, St George's Chapel, Windsor 6, Rhodesia 7, Senator George McGovern 8, He resigned after two weeks to avoid damaging the Democratic campaign with newspaper stories concerning his medical history 9, Willie Whitelaw 10, John Kennedy 11, Idi Amin of Uganda 12, Iceland 13, George Wallace 14, Geoffrey Fisher 15, East Germany

QUIZ 162
SPORT

ℓℓℓ

1 What year did Tom Watson first win the Open?

2 What was boxer Dave Green's nickname?

3 Which cricketer with a famous name scored his 100th century in 1977?

4 Who celebrated a rare victory on English soil by pulling down the goalposts?

5 Who became Scotland's new soccer manager, replacing Willie Ormond?

6 Who joined the ball boys at the 1977 Wimbledon?

7 What was special about the 1977 Wimbledon?

8 Who won the ladies singles?

9 Which country won athletics first world cup?

10 Who was Britain's only individual winner in the 1977 world cup?

11 In which event?

12 Who was Britain's first half-million-pound footballer?

13 Who bought hm for £500,000?

14 And whom did Liverpool sign to replace him?

15 From?

ℓℓℓ

ANSWERS

1, 1975 2, Boy 3, John Edrich 4, Scottish fans after their soccer team's 2-1 win at Wembley 5, Ally Macleod 6, Ball girls 7, It was the centenary of the championships 8, Virginia Wade 9, East Germany 10, Steve Ovett 11, 1500m 12, Kevin Keegan 13, Hamburg 14, Kenny Dalglish 15, Celtic

QUIZ 169
PEOPLE

1. What nationality was the composer Malcolm Williamson?
2. Which organization did Norman Willis work for?
3. What game did Jocky Wilson play?
4. Who wrote a book called *Banjaxed* (1979)?
5. Which church post did Derek Worlock move to in 1976?
6. Who wrote the book *From Apes to Warlords* (1978)?
7. Which famous detective was played on stage by John Wood?
8. Who ran a shop called Sex, on London's King's Road in 1971?
9. Which American presented *Monday Night Football* on TV?
10. Who wrote a book called *The Ocean World*?
11. The creator of *Gideon of Scotland Yard* died in 1973. Who was he?
12. Of which city was Richard Daley mayor?
13. Which activist was sacked for campaigning on behalf of the Soledad brothers?
14. Which Italian film director died in 1974?
15. Who starred in *Mean Streets* (1973)

ANSWERS

1, Australian 2, The TUC 3, Darts 4, Terry Wogan 5, Archbishop of Liverpool 6, Solly Zuckerman 7, Sherlock Holmes 8, Vivienne Westwood 9, Howard Cosell 10, Jacques Cousteau 11, John Creasey 12, Chicago 13, Angela Davis 14, Vittorio de Sica 15, Robert De Niro

QUIZ 164
SCIENCE & TECHNOLOGY

1   Which Australian building, opened in 1973, is made up of huge concrete shell vaults?

2   Why did astronauts destined for Skylab train in a water tank?

3   What launch vehicle was used for the first Skylab?

4   Soviet spacecraft came down to earth by parachute. How did the U.S. method differ?

5   What new method of dealing with illegally parked cars came into use in London?

6   Which country launched Vikings 1 and 2 towards Mars in 1975?

7   The first transatlantic balloon flight was made in 1978. What was the balloon called?

8   What record did cosmonauts Kovalenok and Ivanchenkov set in 1978?

9   Which bridge between Europe and Asia was opened to traffic in 1973?

10 What is the La Grande Complex, which was begun in 1973?

11 Which British mammal was protected from February 1974 by an act of parliament?

12 May 3 in 1978 was observed as Sun Day in support of which cause?

13 Which sports car was to be built in Northern Ireland according to a 1978 announcement?

14 Was the Soviet warplane known as the Backfire a fighter or a bomber?

15 In 1978 the first attempt was made to mine which mineral from the deep ocean floor?

ANSWERS

1, The Sydney Opera House 2, To simulate weightlessness 3, A Saturn V rocket 4, American spacecraft splashed down in the sea 5, Vehicles equipped with hydraulic cranes 6, The United States 7, Double Eagle II 8, A 139-day space endurance record 9, The Bosporus bridge in Istanbul 10, A vast hydroelectric scheme in northern Quebec 11, The badger 12, Solar radiation as a source of energy 13, The Delorean DMC-12 14, A bomber 15, Manganese nodules

QUIZ 165
ARTS & ENTERTAINMENT

1 Who played Mr McKay in *Porridge*?

2 Where was this comedy series set?

3 Who starred as Sally Bowles in the 1973 film *Cabaret*?

4 In which 1975 Stanley Donen film did this actress star with Burt Reynolds and Gene Hackman?

5 Which American actress played Lady Churchill in a TV series?

6 Which actor starred as *Father Brown*?

7 What job did Googie Withers's character have in *Within These Walls*?

8 Where did the Wilkins family of *The Family* documentary series live?

9 Which pair co-starred in *No Honestly*?

10 Who presented *Celebrity Squares* in 1975?

11 Which fix it show started that same year?

12 Who played a stammering Roman emperor on TV?

13 And in which series?

14 Who played Starsky in *Starsky and Hutch*?

15 What colour was their favourite car?

ANSWERS

1, Fulton Mckay 2, In a prison 3, Liza Minelli 4, *Lucky Lady* 5, Lee Remick 6, Kenneth More 7, A prison governor 8, Reading 9, John Alderton and Pauline Collins 10, Bob Monkhouse 11, Jim'll Fix It 12, Derek Jacobi 13, I Claudius 14, Paul Michael Glaser 15, Red and white

QUIZ 166
WORLD EVENTS
1972

1 Where were the Olympics hit by terrorist violence?

2 In what alleged conspiracy were Howard Hunt and Gordon Liddy implicated?

3 Who was leader of Britain's TUC?

4 Whose embassy was hit by bombs in Hanoi in October?

5 Which Russian-born aviator pioneer died on 1 October?

6 Who was Soviet Foreign Minister?

7 Who returned home to Argentina?

8 Which giant bomber was the first of its type shot down in Vietnam?

9 Which new anti-discrimination law came into force in Britain?

10 Who won only 17 electoral college votes against his opponents' 520?

11 Who was the victor in this vote?

12 What were frozen for 90 days in Britain?

13 In which country did the Labor Party come to power in December?

14 Who won the 1972 Nobel Peace Prize?

15 Which former US President died on Boxing Day?

ANSWERS

1, Munich 2, Watergate 3, Vic Feather 4, The French embassy 5, Igor Sikorsky 6, Andrei Gromyko 7, Juan Peron 8, A B-52 9, The Race Relations Act 10, George McGovern 11, Richard Nixon 12, Prices and wages 13, Australia 14, No award was made 15, Harry Truman

QUIZ 167
PEOPLE

●●

1 Whose 1971 autobiography was called *Dear Me*?

2 What government job did Peter Walker hold from 1970–72?

3 Who composed *The Knot Garden*?

4 W H Tilman died in 1977; for what was he well known?

5 Which organization did Ian Trethowan head in 1977?

6 Whose last play was *The Bed Before Yesterday* (1976)?

7 Who was the lead singer with Led Zeppelin?

8 Was Bernard Leach a famous potter or a childcare expert?

9 Which Arab nation's prime minister was murdered in 1971?

10 Of which country was Frederick king until his death in 1972?

11 Where was British ambassador Geoffrey Jackson held hostage?

12 For which English soccer team did Steve Heighway play?

13 Who recorded an album called *Judith* in 1975?

14 In what sport was Roberto Clemente (died 1972) a star?

15 Was Cicero, who died in 1970, a spy, a singer or a fashion designer?

●●

ANSWERS

1, Peter Ustinov 2, Secretary of State for the Environment 3, Michael Tippett 4, He was a mountaineer 5, The BBC 6, Ben Travers 7, Robert Plant 8, He was a potter (died 1979) 9, Jordan's 10, Denmark 11, Uruguay 12, Liverpool 13, Judy Collins 14, Baseball 15, He was a spy for Germany in World War II

QUIZ 168
POT LUCK

✿✿

1 What year did Britain change to decimal currency?

2 On what day of the week did the change take place?

3 Was Leila Khaled a famous 70s supermodel, terrorist, or feminist?

4 Was the 1973 Sunningdale Agreement about Northern Ireland, industrial relations, or global warming?

5 Who kidnapped British trade commissioner James Cross in 1970?

6 Which coins did Britain's Royal Mint stop making in October 1970?

7 In which British city did the events of "Bloody Sunday" take place in 1972?

8 Which miners' leader came to prominence in 1972 as an organizer of "flying pickets"?

9 Why were Guildford and Birmingham in the news in 1974?

10 Which English county officially disappeared on April Fool's Day 1974?

11 What year in the 1970s did Britain have two elections, both won by Labour?

12 What was the popular name for the Middle East War of 1973?

13 Which government department did Margaret Thatcher head in 1970?

14 Who were the two sides in the so-called "cod war"?

15 Who provided the voice of Darth Vader in *Star Wars*?

✿✿

ANSWERS

1, 1971 2, Monday 3, She was a terrorist who hijacked airliners 4, Northern Ireland 5, Quebec extremists 6, Pennies (pre-decimal ones) 7, Londonderry 8, Arthur Scargill 9, Both were hit by terrorist bombs 10, Rutland (as a result of local government reorganization) 11, 1974 12, Yom Kippur War 13, Education and Science 14, Britain and Iceland 15, James Earl Jones

1. For what race was Janet Guthrie the first female entrant?
2. What championship did Margo Oberg of Hawaii win in 1977?
3. In which sport was Mike Hazelwood a world champion?
4. Who came back to Test cricket for England and made a 100?
5. Where did he hit his 100th century?
6. Which Australian businessman upset Australian cricket?
7. Which TV station did he own?
8. What did he do that caused the rumpus?
9. Which England captain helped recruit players for this series?
10. Which teams took part in the first event?
11. Who went to Dubai and upset England's soccer establishment?
12. What job did he leave?
13. Who took over as caretaker manager?
14. In which sport did the 1978 Kangaroos knock out the Lions?
15. For which country did Steve Fenwick play rugby?

ANSWERS

1, The Indy 500 motor race 2, Women's professional surfing world title 3, Water skiing 4, Geoff Boycott 5, Headingley 6, Kerry Packer 7, Channel Nine 8, He signed up top cricketers for his World Series Cricket 9, Tony Greig 10, Australia, West Indies and the Rest of the World 11, Don Revie 12, England soccer manager 13, Ron Greenwood 14, Rugby League 15, Wales

QUIZ 170
WORLD EVENTS
1972

1 Why were 20,000 Scots in Barcelona in May?

2 Where did John Fairfax and Sylvia Cook go?

3 What method of propulsion did they use?

4 Who resigned as Labour's deputy leader?

5 What was he unhappy about?

6 Which 'Big Two' met in Moscow?

7 Where was the Ballymurphy Estate?

8 Which African leader said he was helping the IRA?

9 In which country was the Angela Davis trial held?

10 Where was Andreas Baader arrested?

11 Of what was he accused?

12 Whose warplanes clashed for the first time since 1970?

13 Which two groups were at odds in Burundi?

14 What did the US Supreme Court rule 'unconstitutional'?

15 What serious accident happened near Staines in June?

ANSWERS

1, Glasgow Rangers won the Cup Winners' Cup. 2, Across the Pacific. 3, Oars (they rowed) 4, Roy Jenkins 5, The proposed referendum on EEC membership 6, Nixon and Brezhnev 7, Belfast 8, Gadaffi 9, USA 10, West Germany 11, Terrorism 12, Egypt and Israel's 13, Tutsi and Hutu 14, The death penalty 15, A Trident airliner crashed

QUIZ 171
PEOPLE

●●●

1 In what artistic medium did Dame Gwyneth Jones win fame?

2 What was phyicist Brian Josephson's field of study?

3 Who presented *Royal Heritage* on television in 1977?

4 Who served as Northern Ireland Secretary from 1972–73?

5 Who was the Terry of *Terry and June*?

6 What was Lord Widgery's job?

7 Which youthful violinist made a 1977 debut?

8 Which archaeologist found fossil footprints in Tanzania?

9 Was F R Leavis a scholar or a pop singer?

10 Who wrote *The Honourable Schoolboy*?

11 Which actor starred in the horrow movie *The Creeping Flesh* (1972)?

12 Which Scot moved from Leeds to manage his national soccer team?

13 Which National Hunt jockey learned in 1979 that doctors feared he had less than a year to live?

14 Was Sir James Stirling noted for architecture, finance or owning newspapers?

15 Who presented *Saturday Night People* on television?

●●●

ANSWERS

1, Opera 2, Superconductors 3, Huw Wheldon 4, Willie Whitelaw 5, Terry Scott 6, Lord Chief Justice, from 1971 7, Nigel Kennedy 8, Mary Leakey 9, A scholar (and literary critic) 10, John Le Carré 11, Christopher Lee 12, Jock Stein 13, Bob Champion 14, He was an architect 15, Janet Street-Porter

WORLD EVENTS
1972

1 Who could enter 'the East' for the first time since 1952?

2 Who admitted to faking a biography of Howard Hughes?

3 What set off to look at the great Red Spot?

4 Where was Chou En-lai prime minister?

5 Where was Haiphong under attack?

6 Which writer was refused a Soviet exit visa?

7 Where was General Sanchez assassinated?

8 Which country decided not to join the EEC after all?

9 Which former Ghanaian leader died this year?

10 Which of her relatives did the Queen go to Paris to see?

11 What was their relationship?

12 Why did she make the visit?

13 The boss of the G-men died this year. Who was he?

14 What did his first initial stand for?

15 What organization had he led since the 1930s?

ANSWERS

1, West Berliners 2, Clifford Irving 3, The US Jupiter probe Pioneer 10 4, China 5, North Vietnam 6, Alexander Solzhenitsyn 7, Argentina 8, Norway 9, Kwame Nkrumah 10, The Duke of Windsor 11, He was her uncle 12, He was dying 13, J Edgar Hoover 14, John 15, The FBI (Federal Bureau of Investigation)

QUIZ 179
POT LUCK

●●●

1 What did Arab states stop selling to the West in 1973–74?

2 What did Britain set out to do for the third time in 1970, but fail?

3 Name one of the three Pacific states to join the Commonwealth in 1970.

4 Which South American country was led by Salvador Allende until 1973?

5 What happened to him?

6 Which country was led as premier by John Gorton in 1970?

7 Which superpower joined the United Nations in 1971?

8 Which 70s leader's wife was born Thelma Catharine Ryan?

9 What was Saigon renamed in 1975?

10 Which ageing dictator died in 1975, leaving his country to become a constitutional monarchy?

11 Why were flags waving in British streets in 1977?

12 Which race did Red Rum win for the third time in 1977?

13 Which pop star died at his home in Memphis in 1977?

14 Which tennis tournament celebrated its centenary in 1977?

15 Which British player won the women's singles at the 100th Wimbledon?

●●●

ANSWERS

1, Oil 2, Join the European Community (then the EEC) 3, Fiji, Tonga, Western Samoa 4, Chile 5, He was killed after a right-wing coup. 6, Australia 7, China 8, Richard Nixon's wife Pat 9, Ho Chi Minh City 10, General Franco of Spain 11, Celebrations to mark Queen Elizabeth II's silver jubilee 12, The Grand National 13, Elvis Presley 14, Wimbledon 15, Virginia Wade (1977)

QUIZ 174
ARTS &
ENTERTAINMENT

1 What kind of animal was (and is) Kermit?

2 Whose fall and rise was written by David Nobbs?

3 Who played him on TV?

4 What part did John Barron play?

5 Was *Angels* a TV series about hospitals or fighter pilots?

6 What did Ronnie Barker keep open all hours?

7 Who was his co-star?

8 What was the name of the co-star's character?

9 Who played Purdey in *The New Avengers*?

10 In which series did Brian Murphy and Yootha Joyce co-star?

11 Who played Jesus in a blockbuster TV series?

12 With which painter is the title A Bigger Splash, which featured in a 1974 poster, associated?

13 Who directed the film The Man Who Fell to Earth (1976)?

14 Name the two stars of the 1976 Western Missouri Breaks?

15 Which 1974 horror film featured Texas in the title?

ANSWERS

1. A frog 2. Reginald Perrin's 3. Leonard Rossiter 4. CJ 5. Hospitals 6. A corner shop 7. David Jason 8. Granville 9. Joanna Lumley 10. George and Mildred 11. Robert Powell 12. David Hockney 13. Nicholas Roeg 14. Jack Nicholson and Marlon Brando 15. Texas Chainsaw Massacre

PEOPLE

1 Was Gilbert O'Sullivan American or Irish?

2 What song gave him his first big hit?

3 Of which group was Noddy Holder a member?

4 What was Paul Gadd's stage name?

5 Was Donny the youngest Osmond?

6 Which Roy was with Wizzard?

7 Which 60s group had he played with?

8 Who were Fayette, Sheila and Valerie?

9 With whom did Frankie Valli sing?

10 Benny and Bjorn meant half of … who?

11 Who played Lofty on TV but was quite short really?

12 And with whom did he sing about whispering grass?

13 Were The Tams five men or three girls?

14 Were Chicory Tip a band from Brazil, USA or Britain?

15 Who were George and Olive's singing children?

ANSWERS

1. Irish 2. *Clair* 3. Slade 4. Gary Glitter 5. No 6. Roy Wood 7. The Move 8. The Three Degrees 9. Four Seasons 10. ABBA 11. Don Estelle 12. Windsor Davies 13. Five men 14. They were British 15. The Osmonds

QUIZ 176
POT LUCK

●●

1 Which craze hit the streets on wheels in 1977?

2 What was historic about the British summer of 1976?

3 Who took over as leader of the Liberals in Britain in 1976?

4 And whom did he succeed?

5 Which world leader left the stage in 1977?

6 Which British prime minister resigned unexpectedly in 1976?

7 Which controversial aircraft started passenger services in 1976?

8 Which African city did Israeli commandos raid in 1976 to free hostages?

9 Was 1975 International Women's Year or International Children's Year?

10 What year did Bjorn Borg win his first Wimbledon singles title?

11 Which zoo favourite died in London in 1971?

12 How many Jubilee street parties were there (roughly) in London in 1977: 300, 1500, 4000?

13 Which US rock band played a concert in front of the Pyramids in 1978?

14 What came ashore from the North Sea for the first time in 1975?

15 Which British university enrolled its first students in 1970 without seeing them?

●●

ANSWERS

1, Skateboards 2, Hottest for 250 years 3, David Steel 4, Jeremy Thorpe 5, Mao Tse-tung 6, Harold Wilson 7, Concorde 8, Entebbe (Uganda) 9, International Women's Year 10, 1976 11, Chi-Chi the giant panda 12, 4000 13, The Grateful Dead 14, Oil 15, The Open University

QUIZ 177
SCIENCE & TECHNOLOGY

1 Which disease killed many typically English trees in the early 70s?

2 In 1971 British and New Zealand astronomers found a very distant quasar – what is the name quasar short for?

3 What astronomical event was visible along a path from Brazil to Kenya on June 30, 1973?

4 The lost city of Oplontis was discovered in 1973; where?

5 What did Israeli scientists try raising in vertical pipes rather than in traditional rows: a) cucumbers b) chickens or c) apple trees ?

6 What was unusual about the people of Vilcabamba Valley in Ecuador?

7 Denis Gabor won the Nobel Prize for physics in 1971; of which process was he a pioneer?

8 Where was the tomb of the so-called "wife of the Marquis of Tai", discovered in 1973?

9 Which Apollo spacecraft landed the first four-wheeled manned rover on the Moon?

10 What year was that?

11 What was found during work to build a new House of Commons car park: a) a Tudor fountain b) Charles II's tennis court or c) an execution block?

12 What was being built at Siding Springs in Australia?

13 Which planet did American scientists start to map in 1973?

14 Which was the only Apollo Moon mission not to reach its target?

15 What year was that?

ANSWERS

1, Dutch Elm disease 2, Quasi-stellar object 3, A total eclipse of the sun 4, Italy 5, a) cucumbers 6, Scientists found that many lived to be more than 100 years old 7, Holography 8, China 9, Apollo 15 10, 1971 11, a) a Tudor fountain 12, A new telescope for British and Australian astronomers 13, Venus 14, Apollo 13 15, 1970

QUIZ 170
ARTS &
ENTERTAINMENT

1 Who wrote the music for *Star Wars*?

2 Who played Princess Leia?

3 Who was her real-life mother?

4 What was the super-weapon developed by the evil Empire?

5 What part did Mark Hamill play?

6 Whose was the body inside Darth Vader?

7 Which actor played Obi-Wan Kenobi?

8 What was the name of Han Solo's spaceship?

9 And who was his co-pilot?

10 Was there an actor inside R2D2?

11 Who directed the film?

12 What was the name of Harrison Ford's character?

13 Which British actor played an imperial character named Grand Moff Tarkin?

14 Which animals featured in the 1972 horror movie *The Night of the Lepus?*

15 Which character was originally to be called Starkiller?

ANSWERS

1, John Williams 2, Carrie Fisher 3, Debbie Reynolds 4, The Death Star 5, Luke Skywalker 6, Dave Prowse 7, The Millenium Falcon 8, Chewbacca 9, Yes 10, George Lucas 11, Han Solo 12, Alec Guinness 13, Peter Cushing 14, Rabbits 15, Luke Skywalker

SPORT

1   For which country did Richard Hadlee play Test cricket?

2   Who hit his maiden Test century against Hadlee's team?

3   Where did six England batsmen get out lbw in one innings?

4   Which newly promoted soccer team shot to the top of Division One in 1978?

5   Who was their manager?

6   With which team had he previously won the title?

7   Which Scottish left winger played a big part in this team's success?

8   For whom did Peter Osgood play soccer?

9   In which sport did Ingemar Stenmark win honours?

10   In what event did "Ironmen" compete?

11   Which left hander entered the England cricket scene in 1978?

12   Who won the 1978 Tour de France?

13   How many more Tours would he win?

14   Which English club won the FA Cup for the first time ever in 1978?

15   Was Britain's Hugh Porter a 70s star of a) rugby b) cycle racing or c) golf?

ANSWERS

15, b) cycle racing
11, David Gower 12, Bernard Hinault of France 13, Four 14, Ipswich Town
6, Derby County 7, John Robertson 8, Chelsea 9, Skiing 10, The Triathlon
1, New Zealand 2, Ian Botham 3, Karachi 4, Nottingham Forest 5, Brian Clough

••

1 Which soccer manager said "I've had more clubs than Jack Nicklaus"?

2 What game did Peter Oosterhuis play?

3 Was he American, British or South African?

4 For whom did Mario Kempes star in the 1978 World Cup?

5 Where were the 1978 finals staged?

6 Were England among the finalists?

7 Who were Britain's only representatives?

8 Which South American team got them off to a bad start?

9 Which Scottish player was sent home after a drugs test?

10 For which country did Johnny Rep play?

11 How did they fare in the final?

12 Which Argentines came to London to play football?

13 For whom did they sign?

14 Who was the Londoners' manager at the time?

15 Which batting Gs were in the runs for England?

••

ANSWERS

1, Tommy Docherty. 2, Golf. 3, British. 4, Argentina. 5, Argentina. 6, No. 7, Scotland 8, Peru, with a 3-1 win. 9, Willie Johnstone. 10, Holland. 11, They lost 3-1 to Argentina. 12, Ossie Ardiles and Ricardo Villa. 13, Spurs. 14, Keith Burkinshaw 15, Gooch and Gower.

QUIZ 181
ARTS & ENTERTAINMENT

1 Which radio programme did Derek Cooper present?

2 Which old soldiers moved to BBC Radio in 1974?

3 Who presented radio's *Down Your Way* from 1972?

4 With which sport was he most closely associated?

5 Which DJ was sacked by the BBC in 1970 for a bad joke?

6 Who was Barry the TV film critic?

7 What year was the very last *Goon Show*?

8 Which royal fan missed this last recording?

9 Why?

10 Which carry on show hit the live stage?

11 Which ex-pop singer played Hans Christian Andersen?

12 Who or what was the Herbie of *Herbie Rides Again*?

13 Which Fitzgerald novel was filmed, with Robert Redford?

14 Which was Mel Brooks' spoof Western?

15 Who wrote a play called *Bingo*?

ANSWERS

QUIZ 182
POT LUCK

●●●

1 Where did could visitors see the Duke of Bedford's *Wild Animal Kingdom*?

2 In which James Bond film did Roger Moore and Lois Chiles go into space?

3 Which European country appointed a minister with special responsibility for water to cope with unusual drought conditions?

4 Who designed the ship Great Britain which returned to its home port from the Falkland Islands in 1970?

5 In which sport was Harvey Smith famous?

6 Which country was led by Lee Kuan Yew?

7 Viscount Slim (died 1970) won fame as a soldier in which campaign during World War II?

8 Who commanded the Apollo 13 space mission?

9 Which government office was held by Iain Macleod at the time of his death on July 1970?

10 Of which country was Antonio Salazar (died 1970) dictator?

11 Which famous London at monument did two men climb in 1978?

12 Which British industrial giant was closed by a strike in 1978 over pay?

13 Which famous newspaper was absent from the newstands in 1978 because of an industrial dispute?

14 What did Scots soccer fans pull down at Wembley in 1977: a) their kilts b) the goalposts or c) the twin towers?

15 Which country celebrated its bicentennial in 1976?

●●●

ANSWERS

1, Woburn Abbey in England 2, *Moonraker* 3, Britain (in 1976) 4, I.K. Brunel 5, Show jumping 6, Singapore 7, Burma 8, James Lovell 9, Chancellor of the Exchequer 10, Portugal 11, Nelson's Column 12, Ford 13, *The Times* 14, b) the goalposts 15, The United States

WORLD EVENTS

1972

•••

1 Where were the Winter Olympics held this year?

2 For which group of workers did the Wilberforce inquiry rule on a pay deal?

3 How many rooms were people in the UK asked to heat, to save fuel?

4 Which Western leader walked the Great Wall?

5 Who was his national security adviser?

6 Which British army town was hit by an IRA bomb?

7 Where was President Somoza in charge?

8 Which reclusive millionaire did he meet in March 1972?

9 What was the ERA?

10 And where did it become law?

11 Who launched a look Anglais?

12 Where was direct rule from Westminster imposed?

13 Who was in charge of the directly ruled region?

14 Where was Timothy Davey jailed?

15 How old was he?

•••

ANSWERS

15. Fourteen

11. Yves St Laurent 12. Northern Ireland 13. Willie Whitelaw 14. Turkey

7. Nicaragua 8. Howard Hughes 9. Equal Rights Amendment 10. The USA

1. Tokyo 2. Coal miners 3. One 4. Richard Nixon 5. Henry Kissinger 6. Aldershot

QUIZ 104
PEOPLE
1976

∙∙∙

1 Anais Nin died; for what was she famous?

2 Whose grave was vandalised by anti-hunting saboteurs?

3 Which rock band was sacked by EMI for scandalous behaviour?

4 Which British architect co-designed the Pompidou Centre?

5 In which city was it?

6 Anthony Crosland died; what job did he hold?

7 Who succeeded him in the post?

8 Where was Morarji Desai seeking votes?

9 Which horse did Ginger McCain train?

10 Who was called in to put out a North Sea oil fire?

11 Where did Las Passionara come home?

12 During which war had she earned the name?

13 Which German rocket scientist died in the USA?

14 With which World War II weapon was he associated?

15 Which peacetime programme had he worked on?

∙∙∙

ANSWERS

1, She was a writer (of erotica among other subjects) 2, John Peel's 3, The Sex Pistols 4, Richard Rogers 5, Paris 6, Foreign Secretary 7, Dr David Owen 8, India 9, Red Rum 10, Red Adair 11, Spain 12, Spanish Civil War 13, Wernher von Braun 14, The V-2 15, The *Saturn 5* rocket used in the Apollo Moon landings

QUIZ 105
SPORT

1 For which country did Archie Gemmill play soccer?

2 What position did Pat Jennings play?

3 What was Graham Mourie's sport?

4 For which country?

5 Which Irish team were the first from that country ever to beat the touring All Blacks?

6 Who did England play at rugby for the first time in 1978?

7 What was the result?

8 Which racing driver moved from Ferrari to Brabham?

9 Who became England's first black soccer international?

10 For which club did he play at the time?

11 Which was Britain's first all-seat soccer stadium?

12 Who left Celtic to manage Scotland?

13 And who took over his old job?

14 How many English based players were in Scotland's team against Norway in October 1978?

15 For whom did Greg Cornelsen score four tries in a rugby international?

ANSWERS

1, Scotland 2, Goalkeeper 3, Rugby union 4, New Zealand 5, Munster 6, Argentina 7, A 13-13 draw 8, Niki Lauda 9, Viv Anderson 10, Nottingham Forest 11, Pittodrie, Aberdeen 12, Jock Stein 13, Billy McNeill 14, All 11 15, Australia (and he was a forward)

QUIZ 106
WORLD EVENTS
1972

ffffffffffffffffffffffffffffffffffffffffffff

1 Where was the liner *Queen Elizabeth* destroyed?

2 How was it destroyed?

3 Where was the British embassy burned down in February?

4 In which Gulf state did the Crown Prince seize power?

5 Which millionaire's story was declared 'a fake'?

6 Which country's independent status was recognized by the UK?

7 Which trade union did Ray Buckton lead?

8 Where did Colonel Acheampong seize power?

9 Where was Garfield Todd arrested?

10 Who was the Nazi Butcher of Lyons, on the run in South America?

11 Which suave French singer died on 1 January 1972?

12 Where did the Bloody Sunday shooting take place?

13 Which British army unit was involved?

14 How were Six to become Ten?

15 Who were the extra four?

ffffffffffffffffffffffffffffffffffffffffffff

ANSWERS

1, Hong Kong 2, By fire 3, Dublin 4, Qatar 5, Howard Hughes 6, Bangladesh 7, ASLEF (train drivers) 8, Ghana 9, Rhodesia 10, Klaus Barbie 11, Maurice Chevalier 12, Londonderry 13, Parachute Regiment 14, Four nations were to join the EEC 15, Britain, Ireland, Denmark and Norway

QUIZ 107
ARTS &
ENTERTAINMENT

1 In which crime show did Martin Shaw and Lewis Collins co-star?

2 Whose angel was Farrah Fawcett-Majors?

3 What role had her husband played in a TV series?

4 Who first played James Herriott on TV?

5 Was he a doctor or a vet?

6 Who was Siegfried in the same series?

7 Who played Citizen Smith?

8 Which part of London did he represent radically?

9 And which football team's colours did he sport?

10 Which planet did Superman come from?

11 Which TV programme used this name in its title?

12 Who wrote a play called *Professional Foul*?

13 Which actor called Peter appeared in it?

14 In which TV series did Bernard Hepton play a Belgian cafe owner?

15 Whose greats did Barry Norman celebrate in a TV series?

ANSWERS

PEOPLE

1 Which David wrote *The Tribal Eye*?

2 Which Alan staged plays at Scarborough?

3 Who was veteran actor Felix ..., who died in 1979?

4 Which Gordon quit soccer after losing the sight of an eye?

5 Which Ronnie played Fletcher?

6 Which Franny played for England?

7 Which Pat was champion jockey in 1974?

8 Which Nick was PGA champion in 1978?

9 Which Andrew wrote the music for *Jeeves*?

10 Which Denis was married to Maggie?

11 Which Norman, who died in 1978, was the royal dressmaker?

12 Which Dame Kathleen was a noted archaeologist (and also died in 1978)?

13 Which David made the film *Ryan's Daughter*?

14 Which Ally said the Scots would win the World Cup?

15 Who began his career with West Bromwich Albion before later going on to captain Manchester United and England?

ANSWERS

1, Attenborough 2, Ayckbourne 3, Aylmer 4, Banks 5, Barker 6, Lee 7, Eddery 8, Faldo 9, Lloyd Webber 10, Thatcher 11, Hartnell 12, Kenyon 13, Lean 14, Macleod 15, Bryan Robson

QUIZ 189
POT LUCK

🐛🐛🐛🐛🐛🐛🐛🐛🐛🐛🐛🐛🐛🐛🐛🐛🐛🐛🐛🐛🐛🐛🐛🐛🐛🐛🐛🐛🐛🐛🐛🐛🐛🐛🐛🐛🐛

1 Where in Britain was the new NEC opened in 1976?

2 What did NEC stand for?

3 Which Canadian city hosted the 1976 Olympic Games?

4 Which clock stopped at 3.45 a.m. on 5th August 1975?

5 Whose statue was unveiled in Parliament Square, London in 1973?

6 For what was Mick Jagger fined £200 in January 1970?

7 Whose grave in Highgate, London, was daubed and damaged by vandals in 1970?

8 Which British TV soap reached its 1000th episode in August 1970?

9 Who or what were Chia-Chia and Ching-Ching, seen in London in 1974?

10 Which British cathedral begun in 1904 was not dedicated until 1978?

11 Who was BBC Radio One's first woman DJ (1970)?

12 What was Ekofisk?

13 Where did the West Gate Bridge collapse in October 1970?

14 In which country did postmen go on strike for the first time in 1971?

15 ?

🐛🐛🐛🐛🐛🐛🐛🐛🐛🐛🐛🐛🐛🐛🐛🐛🐛🐛🐛🐛🐛🐛🐛🐛🐛🐛🐛🐛🐛🐛🐛🐛🐛🐛🐛🐛🐛

ANSWERS

1, Birmingham 2, National Exhibition Centre 3, Montreal 4, Big Ben 5, Sir Winston Churchill 6, Possession of cannabis 7, Karl Marx 8, *Coronation Street* 9, Giant pandas 10, Liverpool 11, Anne Nightingale 12, A Norwegian oil field in the North Sea 13, Melbourne, Australia 14, United Kingdom 15,

QUIZ 190
SPORT

1 Who caused a shock by beating Muhammad Ali in Las Vegas?

2 What happened in the return fight?

3 Which Scottish boxer won the lightweight world title in 1979?

4 Who was Alan Mullery managing to promotion?

5 Where was boxer Maurice Hope born?

6 Who kept 27 clean sheets for Liverpool?

7 Who became Britain's first million-pound footballer?

8 Who signed him?

9 For which team had this player made his debut aged only 16?

10 In which match did he score an important only goal?

11 Who was England's fastest bowler against Australia in 1979?

12 What toy animal did an Australian player bring out to greet Derek Randall?

13 Who was the England captain who held on to the Ashes?

14 Where was the first day/night cricket match staged?

15 Which golfer was known as Fuzzy?

ANSWERS

1, Leon Spinks, 2, Ali won, 3, Jim Watt, 4, Brighton, 5, Antigua, 6, Ray Clemence 7, Trevor Francis, 8, Brian Clough, for Nottingham Forest, 9, Birmingham City 10, The European Cup Final, 11, Bob Willis, 12, A plastic snake, 13, Mike Brearley 14, Sydney, 15, US golfer Frank Zoeller

QUIZ 191
WORLD EVENTS
1972

●●●

1 Which two Middle East countries announced in 1972 that they would merge in 1973?

2 How many new countries had joined the Six by the end of this year?

3 Where in London were Tutankhamun's treasures on show?

4 Where was Sheikh Karume assassinated?

5 Which country did Queen Juliana reign over?

6 Which statue by Michelangelo was attacked in Rome?

7 Who was the first US President to visit the USSR?

8 What did Michel Siffre do for 205 days in Texas?

9 What kind of airliner came down in Britain's worst ever air disaster?

10 From which country did President Heinemann come to visit the UK?

11 Who was world motor racing champion?

12 Where did voters end the Catholic Church's special position in the constitution?

13 Where is Managua?

14 And what disaster struck there this year?

15 What sank in the Solent in March 1972, killing five people?

●●●

ANSWERS

1. Egypt and Libya 2. Three 3. The British Museum 4. Zanzibar 5. The Netherlands 6. The Pieta 7. Nixon 8. He stayed underground, in a cave, 9. A Trident 10. West Germany 11. Emerson Fittipaldi 12. The Irish Republic 13. Nicaragua 14. An earthquake 15. A hovercraft

QUIZ 192
SPORT

1 Who became the youngest Open golf champion of the century?

2 What was tennis star Tanner's first name?

3 For whom did Joel Garner bowl?

4 Who won her 20th Wimbledon title in 1979?

5 When had she won her first?

6 Which was the first British soccer club to wear sponsored shirts?

7 What action did TV companies take?

8 Which horse won the Derby by seven lengths?

9 Who managed Sheffield Wednesday in 1979?

10 Who scored Arsenal's winning goal in the 1979 Cup Final?

11 Which country won the cricket championship after 103 years of trying?

12 Who won the first world indoors bowls championship?

13 Who was the 1979 WBC heavyweight champion?

14 Who announced he was retiring from the ring in the same year?

15 From which post in football did Alan Hardaker retire?

•••

ANSWERS

1, Severiano Ballesteros 2, Roscoe 3, West Indies 4, Billie Jean King 5, 1966 6, Liverpool 7, They refused to show the logo on screen 8, Troy 9, Jack Charlton 10, Alan Sunderland 11, Essex 12, David Bryant 13, Larry Holmes 14, Muhammad Ali 15, Secretary of the Football League

QUIZ 199
PEOPLE

1 Which singer appeared in the 1977 film *Oh God*?

2 Which actor starred in *Taxi Driver*?

3 Which Canadian leader died in 1979?

4 Who wrote the novel *Ragtime*?

5 What was Frank Costello's line of work?

6 What nationality was Edouard Daladier?

7 Was Mary Daly well known in the USA as a theologian or an actress?

8 Where did Sir Dawda Jawara become president in 1970?

9 Who wrote the play *Move Over Mrs Markham*?

10 Who recorded a 1977 album called *My Aim Is True*?

11 Who starred on TV in *No That's Me Over There*?

12 Who were the co-stars of *Not Only, But Also*?

13 Who made a film called *Big Banana Feet* in 1975?

14 Who were the co-stars of the film *The Man Who Would Be King*?

15 Who wrote a book called *Superwoman*?

ANSWERS

1, John Denver 2, Robert De Niro 3, John Diefenbaker 4, E L Doctorow 5, He was a US racketeer (died 1973) 6, French 7, A theologian 8, The Gambia 9, Ray Cooney 10, Elvis Costello 11, Ronnie Corbett 12, Peter Cook and Dudley Moore 13, Billy Connolly 14, Michael Caine and Sean Connery 15, Shirley Conran

QUIZ 194
SCIENCE & TECHNOLOGY

1 How many crewmen from each Apollo mission actually landed on the Moon?

2 Anthony Hewish and Sir Martin Ryle were 70s leaders in which field of science?

3 What was Freddy, built by scientists at Edinburgh University in 1973: a) a computerized robot b) an electric car or c) Scotland's first space rocket?

4 Which ship was surveying the ocean floor during the 70s: a) Endeavour b) Deep Quest or c) Glomar Challenger?

5 What did the initials ESRO stand for?

6 Which agency took over ESRO's work in 1974?

7 Was Europa II a proposal for a space rocket, a super train, or a successor to Concorde?

8 What was Blue Streak, on which Britain stopped work in the 70s: a jet fighter, a rocket, or a superfast car?

9 What happened to the three-man crew of the 1971 *Soyuz 11* flight?

10 Where did the Russians send their Lunokhod probe in 1970?

11 What kind of craft did this mission release for further exploration?

12 Was Salyut an orbital space station, a rocket launcher, or the name of a dog flown around the Moon by the Russians?

13 How many astronauts could live on board the US Skylab space station?

14 What did two men from Mississippi claim to have been captured by in1973?

15 What was JIM, shown to the world in 1973?

ANSWERS

1. Two 2. Astronomy 3. a) a computerized robot 4. c) Glomar Challenger 5. European Space Research Organization 6. The European Space Agency 7. A space rocket (abandoned in 1973) 8. A rocket 9. They died during the return to Earth when the cabin pressure failed 10. To the Moon 11. An unmanned robot vehicle 12. An orbital space station 13. Three 14. Aliens (creatures with crab claws!), who released them after examining them 15. A deep-sea diving suit

ARTS & ENTERTAINMENT

1 Which series set in a London school did Phil Redmond create for TV?

2 Which role did Linda Gray play in *Dallas*?

3 Who was her husband?

4 And who played his mother?

5 What was the name of her character?

6 Which big-voiced singer played Clayton Farlow?

7 Who played Bobby?

8 And who was Pam?

9 What role did Charlene Tilton play?

10 How did Bobby come back from the dead?

11 Who played Rumpole on TV?

12 Who created the character?

13 What was this writer's day job?

14 Which Dennis was sure it would be alright on the night?

15 Which African river was the subject of a 1972 drama documentary about the search for its source?

ANSWERS

1. *Grange Hill* 2. Sue Ellen 3. J R 4. Barbara Bel Geddes 5. Miss Ellie 6. Howard Keel 7. Patrick Duffy 8. Victoria Principal 9. Lucy Ewing 10. He materialised in Pam's shower 11. Leo McKern 12. John Mortimer 13. Lawyer 14. Dennis Norden 15. The Nile

QUIZ 196
POT LUCK

1 How many pennies made up a shilling in Britain's pre-1971 currency?

2 What was a shilling worth in new pence after decimalization?

3 What was the smallest denomination in the new currency?

4 Which Scottish explorer's centenary was marked in 1973 by a service in Zambia?

5 On which project did a test boring begin in 1973?

6 Which republic celebrated its 50th anniversary in 1973?

7 Which animal was protected by law from 1973 in the UK?

8 What was Charles Conrad doing in space in 1973?

9 What were Britons urged to do in 1973 to green the environment?

10 Why was the working week shorter in Britain from January 1, 1974?

11 What was the winged Jaguar of 1973?

12 What was the name of the fictional hospital in the 1975 TV series Angels?

13 Which bridge linking Europe and Asia opened in 1973?

14 Which former US President died in 1973?

15 What did his middle initial (B) stand for?

ANSWERS

1, 12 2, 5p 3, 1p 4, David Livingstone 5, Channel Tunnel 6, Turkey 7, Badger 8, He was on Skylab, the first US space station 9, Plant a Tree 10, The three-day week came into effect, to save energy 11, A new warplane 12, St Angela's 13, Bosporus Bridge 14, Lyndon Johnson 15, Baines

SPORT

●●

1 Who was measured to be the fastest bowler in the world?

2 How fast was he timed at?

3 Who ranked second?

4 Was there an English bowler in the top ten?

5 Who won the 1979 Formula One drivers' championship?

6 Which yacht race ended in disaster?

7 What was different about the Ryder Cup team from now on?

8 Who were the first two non-Britons to compete?

9 Did the new-look team triumph in 1979?

10 Who won his sixth speedway world title?

11 Which up and coming French driver signed for McLaren?

12 What work did James Hunt turn to having left the track?

13 Who were the decade's last Rugby League cupwinners?

14 Who won the 1979 Grand National?

15 To whom was Chris Evert married when she lost the 1979 Wimbledon final?

●●

ANSWERS

1, Jeff Thomson of Australia 2, 91.86 mph 3, Michael Holdings of the West Indies 4, No 5, Jody Scheckter 6, The Fastnet race, the last event in the Admiral's Cup 7, It included Europeans, as well as British golfers 8, Severiano Ballesteros and Antonio Garrido of Spain 9, No, USA won 10, Ivan Mauger 11, Alain Prost 12, TV 13, Widnes 14, Rubstic 15, John Lloyd

QUIZ 198
WORLD EVENTS
1973

1 The world's oldest head of state died in June: who?
2 Who suggested people should vote Labour to oppose EEC membership?
3 Which space station received its first US crew?
4 Which group of people occupied Wounded Knee?
5 Which two countries were joining the UN?
6 Where were students expelled for demanding a black university rector?
7 Who was President Nixon's counsel, telling what he knew of Watergate?
8 What was H R Haldeman's familiar name?
9 Which leader made an historic first trip to Israel?
10 Who was Israel's eye-patch-wearing defence ministe?
11 Which plane was nicknamed Concordski?
12 At which air show did one crash in June 1973?
13 Which billionaire's grandson was kidnapped?
14 Which TV show did the Russians denounce as imperialistic?
15 Which East German leader died on 1 August 1973?

ANSWERS

1, Eamon de Valera of Ireland 2, Enoch Powell 3, Skylab 4, Native Americans 5, East and West Germany 6, South Africa 7, John Dean 8, Bob 9, West Germany's Willy Brandt 10, Moshe Dayan 11, The Soviet TU-144 12, Paris 13, Paul Getty's 14, Sesame Street 15, Walter Ulbricht

PEOPLE

1 Which US novelist, author of USA, died in 1970?

2 Who was the author of *The Realm of Gold* (1975)?

3 Where was Jean Drapeau a political leader?

4 What branch of science was Frank D Drake involved with?

5 From where was Jose Napoleon Duarte exiled in 1972?

6 Who wrote a book called *The Whole Truth*?

7 Was Annegret Richter a German athlete, revolutionary or musician?

8 Which jazz 'duke' died in 1974?

9 Which actress starred in the 1971 film *Klute*?

10 She also appeared in which other 70s film, about a nuclear accident?

11 Who directed the movie *Cabaret*?

12 Was he best known for his dancing or singing?

13 Which astronaut became a US senator in 1975?

14 What was William Henry Hare's nickname?

15 Which sport did he play?

ANSWERS

1, John Dos Passos 2, Margaret Drabble 3, Canada (Montreal) 4, Radio astronomy 5, El Salvador 6, John Erlichman 7, Athlete, she won the 100 m at the 1976 Olympics 8, Duke Ellington 9, Jane Fonda 10, The China Syndrome 11, Bob Fosse 12, Dancing 13, John Glenn 14, Dusty 15, Rugby Union

QUIZ 200
WORLD EVENTS
1973

1 In which country did Picasso die?

2 Where did Andropov get into the Politburo?

3 From which post did Richard Kleindienst resign?

4 Which party lost power in the Irish Republic?

5 Who denied she would marry a horse-riding captain?

6 Where was Governor Richard Sharples murdered?

7 Which Nazi leader's death was confirmed in 1973?

8 Which junior defence minister quit in a sex scandal?

9 Where was there civil war between a government and Palestinian guerillas?

10 Whom did Princess Anne announce she would marry?

11 Who spoke of the unacceptable face of capitalism?

12 Of which hearings was Senator Sam Ervin chairman?

13 Where was businessman Charles Lockwood kidnapped?

14 Where did Soviet leader Brezhnev visit in June 1973?

15 Which architect was named in a British inquiry into public sector fraud?

ANSWERS

1. France 2. USSR 3. US Attorney General 4. Fianna Fáil 5. Princess Anne 6. Bermuda 7. Martin Bormann 8. Lord Lambton 9. Lebanon 10. Captain Mark Phillips 11. Edward Heath 12. The Senate Watergate hearings 13. Argentina 14. The United States 15. John Poulson

QUIZ 201
POT LUCK

1 Where was TV's *Crown Court* set?

2 Which TV show did John Craven present for children?

3 Where did Michael Manley win an election in 1972?

4 Who reached the top with *Without You*?

5 Where was direct rule imposed in 1972?

6 Which country launched Pioneer 10?

7 At which planet was it targeted?

8 Who presented *Film 72*?

9 Who played John Alderton's ex-wife in *My Wife Next Door*?

10 Which city was *Pebble Mill* broadcast from?

11 Complete the game show title: *Sale of* …

12 Who won the 1972 European soccer championship?

13 Which jockey rode the Derby winner in 1972?

14 How many points was a Rugby Union try worth in 1972?

15 What had been the pre-1972 value of such a try?

ANSWERS

1, Fulchester 2, *Newsround* 3, Jamaica 4, Harry Nilsson 5, Northern Ireland 6, USA 7, Jupiter 8, Barry Norman 9, Hannah Gordon 10, Birmingham 11, *the Century* 12, West Germany 14, Four points 15, Three points

QUIZ 202
ARTS & ENTERTAINMENT

1 Who starred in a remake of *The Saint* in 1978?

2 Which actor had appeared as the Saint in the 60s on TV?

3 What was the Saint's fictional name?

4 Who took over *The Generation Game* in 1978?

5 Who presented *3-2-1*?

6 Which Hardy novel was televised with Alan Bates in the starring role?

7 For which series was a replica of the Beagle built?

8 Who wrote *Butterflies* for TV?

9 And who starred in ithe series?

10 In which series did the Campbells and Tates feature?

11 Who played *Wonder Woman*?

12 Complete the title: *Battlestar* ...?

13 Where did Terry and Arthur go for a drink?

14 And in what series?

15 Who played Arthur?

ANSWERS

1, Ian Ogilvy 2, Roger Moore 3, Simon Templar 4, Larry Grayson 5, Ted Rogers 6, *The Mayor of Casterbridge* 7, *The Voyage of Charles Darwin* 8, Carla Lane 9, Wendy Craig 10, *Soap* 11, Lynda Carter 12, Galactica 13, The Winchester Club 14, *Minder* 15, George Cole

QUIZ 209
PEOPLE
ALL DIED IN 1973

1 With which famous reference work was William Benton associated?

2 What was Abebe Bikila famous for?

3 What had forced him to give up this pursuit in 1969?

4 Which famous poet was a friend of Christopher Isherwood?

5 What were this poet's first names?

6 In which country was Arthur Calwell a politician?

7 What was Alan Cobham famous for?

8 Whose real name was Sean O'Feeney?

9 Where was Gustaf VI Adolf king?

10 In which country was Otto Klemperer born?

11 What did Edward Lockspeiser write about?

12 What nationality was actress Anna Magnani?

13 Who was known as the 'Flying Finn'?

14 What sport did Wilfred Rhodes star in?

15 Which Hollywood Betty died in 1973?

ANSWERS

1, *Encyclopaedia Britannica* 2, Running marathons 3, A car crash left him paralysed 4, W H Auden 5, Wystan Hugh 6, Australia 7, He was an Australian pioneer aviator 8, John Ford, film director 9, Sweden 10, Germany 11, Music 12, Italian 13, Paavo Nurmi 14, Cricket 15, Grable

QUIZ 204
POT LUCK

1 Which European country passed anti-aerosol laws in 1978?

2 Who took over from Mike Brearley as England cricket captain?

3 To which country did the British Foreign Secretary apologise in 1978?

4 Who topped the US charts with *Baby Come Back*?

5 From which country did Donald Woods flee?

6 What was his job?

7 Who was expelled from India's Congress Party in 1978?

8 Who starred as Blake in *Blake's Seven*?

9 Whose *Big Night* began on ITV in 1978?

10 What did Bob Hoskins sell in *Pennies From Heaven*?

11 Who presented the *South Bank Show*?

12 Where was the Le Mons Hotel?

13 On which Caribbean island did Princess Margaret holiday?

14 Who was ITN's first woman newsreader?

15 What nationality was the first non-Russian cosmonaut?

ANSWERS

QUIZ 205
SCIENCE & TECHNOLOGY

1 What was unusual about the Royal Navy's 1973 minesweeper HMS *Wilton*?

2 Which spacecraft was the fastest ever to leave the Earth, in 1972?

3 In 1973 a space probe crossed the orbit of Hades, the outermost moon of ... which planet?

4 What kind of animal was Washoe who impressed US scientists with his learning ability?

5 Which continent revealed its first-ever complete prehistoric reptile fossil in 1971?

6 On what habit did the Royal College of Physicians issue a second danger-warning in 1971?

7 Who found the "Genesis rock" in 1971?

8 What kind of satellite was *Intelsat 4*, launched in 1971?

9 Two Asian countries launched their second satellites in 1971; who?

10 What happened to the Russian *Luna 18* probe after it had circled the Moon 54 times?

11 The *Mariner 9* space probe photographed Phobos; where is Phobos?

12 In 1970 which was the only "developed" country to refuse to have television?

13 Percy Shaw died in 1976, what motoring aid did he invent?

14 Where were a previously unknown "Stone Age" people called the Tasaday "discovered" in the early 70s?

15 What weighed more than 350 tonnes and landed at Heathrow for the first time in January 1970?

ANSWERS

1. It was made of non-magnetic glass fibre 2, *Pioneer 10* 3, Jupiter 4, Chimpanzee 5, Antarctica 6, Cigarette smoking 7, Apollo 15 astronauts on the Moon (it was the oldest rock sample found) 8, Communications 9, China and Japan 10, It crashed 11, It's the largest moon of Mars 12, South Africa 13, Cats eyes 14, The Philippines 15, A Boeing 747

QUIZ 206
ARTS &
ENTERTAINMENT

1 Who played a scarecrow for children on TV?

2 Which doctor popped in and out of a blue phone box?

3 Who played a rich man called Richard De Vere?

4 Name the series

5 And his co-star?

6 Who presented *Give Us A Clue*?

7 Complete the title: *Not the* …?

8 Which rubber-faced comic made a mark in this show?

9 Who starred in *Shoestring*?

10 What model car did he drive in the series?

11 And in and around which city was it set?

12 In which show did Boss Hogg appear?

13 Which actress starred in *Testament of Youth* (1979)?

14 On whose book was it based?

15 Which small but voracious fish gave this 1977 horror film its title?

ANSWERS

1, Jon Pertwee 2, Dr Who 3, Peter Bowles 4, To The Manor Born 5, Penelope
Keith 6, Michael Aspel 7, Nine O'Clock News 8, Rowan Atkinson 9, Trevor Eve
10, A Cortina 11, Bristol 12, The Dukes of Hazzard 13, Cheryl Campbell 14, Vera
Brittain's 15, Piranha

WORLD EVENTS

1973

●●

1 Which President said he'd stay in office indefinitely?

2 Where were 13 air force officers executed for treason?

3 What kind of craft did Britain first send to fight off Icelandic gunboats?

4 What fish was causing all the bother?

5 What fell by £4 billion on one day in January?

6 Which US airlines decided to stay subsonic?

7 Which airliner did they refuse to buy?

8 In which city was the ceasefire in Vietnam signed?

9 Which former US president died in Texas this year?

10 Who were allowed on the London Stock Exchange for the first time?

11 Whose coffin was stolen in France?

12 Whose jets shot down a Libyan airliner in February this year?

13 What part of the UK came to a halt in a general strilke?

14 What was the Hanoi Hilton?

15 Why was getting to work hard for Londoners on 27 February?

●●

ANSWERS

1, Marcos of the Philippines 2, Morocco 3, A super tug 4, Cod 5, Share prices in London 6, Pan Am and TWA 7, Concorde 8, Paris 9, Lyndon Johnson 10, Women 11, Marshal Petain's 12, Israel's 13, Northern Ireland 14, A prisoner of war camp 15, The trains were on strike

QUIZ 208
POT LUCK

●●

1 In which country did the Old Groaner die?

2 Who was this person?

3 Who was his film partner, famous as a wisecracking comic?

4 Which Brazilian soccer star retired in 1977?

5 Where did marines storm a train to rescue hostages?

6 In which TV comedy series did Connie Booth play Polly?

7 Where did writers and scholars issue Charter 77?

8 After whom was Paris's new arts centre named?

9 Of which country did Jack Lynch become prime minister?

10 Who was the first Arab leader to visit Israel?

11 Which British politician became president of the EEC Commission?

12 Who launched a mini-TV in the UK?

13 Where in Africa was an archbishop murdered for criticizing the government?

14 Who was that country's leader?

15 Who was Britain's new Foreign Secretary in February 1977?

●●

ANSWERS

1, Spain 2, Bing Crosby 3, Bob Hope 4, Pele 5, The Netherlands 6, *Fawlty Towers* 7, Czechoslovakia 8, Georges Pompidou 9, Republic of Ireland 10, Anwar Sadat 11, Roy Jenkins 12, Clive Sinclair 13, Uganda 14, Idi Amin 15, David Owen

QUIZ 209
ARTS &
ENTERTAINMENT

1 In which play did Alan Howard play Theseus in 1970?

2 Which queen did Eileen Atkins play in *Vivat! Vivat Regina!*?

3 Who wrote *The Philanthropist*?

4 Who wrote *Forget-Me-Not Lane*?

5 Which new play by Simon Gray was staged in 1971?

6 Who wrote a play called *Old Times*?

7 Which two actor-Johnnies co-starred in *Veterans*?

8 Complete the title: *Lloyd George Knew* …?

9 Which Hollywood actress starred on stage in *Applause*?

10 Which composer was the central figure in *Amadeus*?

11 And which lesser figure plotted his downfall?

12 In which play did Alf Garnett have a stage success in 1979?

13 What's this actor's name?

14 Which comedienne made a mark in *Talent* in 1979?

15 Who created the musical *Company*?

ANSWERS

1, *A Midsummer Night's Dream* 2, Elizabeth I 3, Christopher Hampton 4, Peter Nicholls 5, *Butley* 6, Harold Pinter 7, John Mills and John Gielgud 8, *My Father* 9, Lauren Bacall 10, Mozart 11, Salieri 12, *Death of a Salesman* 13, Warren Mitchell 14, Victoria Wood 15, Stephen Sondheim

QUIZ 210
ARTS &
ENTERTAINMENT

1. In what future year was the 1975 film *Death Race* ... set?

2. Which 1973 film features Scott Joplin's *The Entertainer* among its musical themes?

3. Who directed this film?

4. In which 1978 film did Gregory Peck play the Nazi Dr Mengele?

5. Which 50s pop star was played in a 1978 biopic by Gary Busey?

6. Which book by E Nesbit provided Jenny Agutter with a 1972 starring role?

7. Which 1978 film starring Sylvia Kristel became a soft-porn success around the world?

8. For which 1977 film did Diane Keaton win a best-actress Oscar?

9. Who played Willy Wonka in a 1971 film of Roald Dahl's children's book about a chocolate factory?

10. Which mythological seafarer went on a Golden Voyage in a 1973 film?

11. Who played the tough cop Popeye Doyle in *The French Connection* (1972)?

12. Which 1972 film told the story of the last tsar of Russia?

13. Which TV series about bus drivers was turned into a 1972 film?

14. Which 1972 film was Alfred Hitchcock's first British movie for 20 years?

15. Which British composer's *Third Symphony* was first heard in 1972?

ANSWERS

1, 2000 2, *The Sting* 3, George Roy Hill 4, *The Boys From Brazil* 5, Buddy Holly 6, *The Railway Children* 7, *Emmanuelle* 8, *Annie Hall* 9, Gene Wilder 10, Sinbad 11, Gene Hackman 12, *Nicholas and Alexandra* 13, *On The Buses* 14, *Frenzy* 15, Michael Tippett's

WORLD EVENTS

1973

1 What government post did Lord Carrington hold?

2 Where was *Summerland*?

3 And what happened there?

4 Where did W H Auden die in September this year?

5 In which country had he lived for many years before returning to Britain?

6 Which Grand Prix driver quit on the eve of his 100th race?

7 Where did Carl Gustaf become king?

8 Which Chilean leader was killed during a coup?

9 Which famous Finnish runner died in October?

10 Which raw material cost 70% more from October?

11 Which war provoked the increase?

12 What did the initials LBC mean to radio listeners?

13 Which famous cellist died this year?

14 With what was Spiro Agnew charged before he quit as US Vice President?

15 What were the British government printing 16 million of?

ANSWERS

1, Defence minister. 2, Douglas, Isle of Man. 3, 30 people died in a fire. 4, Vienna 5, The United States. 6, Jackie Stewart. 7, Sweden. 8, President Allende. 9, Paavo Nurmi. 10, Oil. 11, The Middle East War or Yom Kippur War. 12, London Broadcasting Company. 13, Pablo Casals. 14, Tax evasion. 15, Petrol ration books

QUIZ 212
PEOPLE

••

All these people were 1970s Presidents. But where?

1 Houari Boumedienne

2 Juan Peron

3 Luis Echeverria Alvarez

4 Alfredo Stroessner

5 Siaka Stevens

6 Jacobus Fouche

7 Habib Bourguiba

8 Idi Amin

9 Jimmy Carter

10 Nguyen Van Thieu

11 Hastings Banda

12 V V Giri

13 General Suharto

14 Sir Seretse Khama

15 Georges Pompidou

••

ANSWERS

1, Algeria 2, Argentina 3, Mexico 4, Paraguay 5, Sierra Leone 6, South Africa 7, Tunisia 8, Uganda 9, USA 10, South Vietnam 11, Malawi 12, India 13, Indonesia 14, Botswana 15, France

SPORT
1972 OLYMPICS

1 Which event did Valery Borzoi win?

2 Which country won gold and silver in the men's 400 metres?

3 Who won the men's Marathon?

4 Who won the women's Marathon?

5 Who was the most successful sportsman of the Games?

6 Who were Olympic soccer champions?

7 Which two events did Olga Korbut win?

8 What event did Richard Meade win for Britain?

9 How many rowing medals did Britain win?

10 In which event did Francois Daniel Morelon star?

11 What nationality was Shane Gould?

12 Who was the British gold medal heroine in athletics?

13 Which event did she win?

14 Who won both women's sprint gold medals (100 and 200 metres)?

15 Which event did Heide Rosendhal win?

ANSWERS

1, Men's 100 and 200 metres 2, USA 3, Frank Shorter 4, There was no women's marathon 5, Mark Spitz 6, Poland 7, Floor exercises and balance beam: 8, Individual Three Day Event 9, None 10, Cycling (sprint) 11, Australian 12, Mary Peters 13, Women's pentathlon 14, Renate Stecher of East Germany 15, Women's long jump

QUIZ 214
WORLD EVENTS
1974

1. In which country did ballet star Mikhail Baryshnikov defect?
2. On which island were Turkish and Greek communities fighting?
3. What was the MRCA?
4. By what name was it later known?
5. Where was Haile Selassie overthrown?
6. Which British politician went campaigning by hovercraft?
7. Who won the October general election in Britain?
8. Who led the winning party?
9. Who became Britain's sports minister?
10. Who took over as US President in August?
11. Whom did he choose as his Vice-President?
12. David Jenkins and Alan Pascoe won European gold for Britain in which sport?
13. Which group of workers in Britain received a 58% pay rise?
14. Who was 'Lucky' and had disappeared?
15. Which title did Helen Morgan give up?

ANSWERS

1, Canada 2, Cyprus 3, The European Multi-Role-Combat Aircraft 4, Tornado 5, Ethiopia 6, Jeremy Thorpe 7, Labour 8, Harold Wilson 9, Denis Howell 10, Gerald Ford 11, Nelson Rockefeller 12, Athletics 13, Nurses 14, Lord Lucan 15, Miss World

QUIZ 215
ARTS & ENTERTAINMENT

●●

1 Who sang *Everything is Beautiful* in 1970?

2 *ABC* and *The Love You Save* were US hits for – whom?

3 Which wildlife suffered most when Pink Floyd played at Crystal Palace?

4 Who was backed by the Full Tilt Boogie Band?

5 Where was the Shea Stadium?

6 Who recorded an album called *Beaucoups of Blues*?

7 Where did Jimi Hendrix play his last live gig?

8 Which group made the film *Gimme Shelter*?

9 Who began legal proceedings to dissolve the Beatles?

10 Who wrote a book called *Tarantula*?

11 Who sang *I Hear You Knockin'*?

12 Who played Pierre in the 1972 BBC television adaptation of *War and Peace?*

13 And whose tears were they singing about in 1970?

14 Who recorded an album track called *The Immigrant Song*?

15 Which 1970 group later became 10CC?

●●

ANSWERS

1. Ray Stevens 2. Jackson Five 3. Fish in a lake were killed, possibly by noise 4. Janis Joplin 5. New York 6. Ringo Starr 7. Isle of Wight Festival 8. The Rolling Stones 9. Paul McCartney 10. Bob Dylan 11. Dave Edmunds 12. Anthony Hopkins 13. Tears of a Clown 14. Led Zeppelin 15. Hotlegs

QUIZ 216
PEOPLE

🎵🎵🎵🎵🎵🎵🎵🎵🎵🎵🎵🎵🎵🎵🎵🎵🎵🎵🎵🎵🎵🎵🎵🎵🎵🎵🎵🎵🎵🎵🎵🎵🎵🎵🎵🎵🎵🎵

1 Which David was BBC TV's top athletics commentator?

2 Which Ken became an MP in 1970?

3 Which Eric played guitar better than most?

4 Which Michael played Frank?

5 Which Henry lost his boxing crown?

6 Which Shirley wrote *Superwoman*?

7 Which Harold wrote *No Man's Land*?

8 Which Harold left Number 10 unexpectedly?

9 Which Arthur won Wimbledon in 1975?

10 Which Malcolm wore Number 9 for Newcastle?

11 Which Clay drove racing cars?

12 Which David played Hutch?

13 Which Anna read the TV news?

14 Which actress Sybil died in 1976?

15 Which Stephen wrote *A little Night Music*?

🎵🎵🎵🎵🎵🎵🎵🎵🎵🎵🎵🎵🎵🎵🎵🎵🎵🎵🎵🎵🎵🎵🎵🎵🎵🎵🎵🎵🎵🎵🎵🎵🎵🎵🎵🎵🎵🎵

ANSWERS

1, Coleman 2, Clarke 3, Clapton 4, Crawford (Frank Spencer) 5, Cooper 6, Conran 7, Pinter 8, Wilson 9, Ashe 10, Macdonald 11, Reggazoni 12, Soul 13, Ford 14, Thorndike 15, Sondheim

QUIZ 217
POT LUCK

●●●

1 Which US city suffered power cuts in 1977?

2 Who sang *I Feel Love*?

3 Which film began with the words "A long time ago in a galaxy far, far away …"?

4 Which British athlete was European 1500 metres champion in 1977?

5 Which new spacecraft took to the air for the first time?

6 Which nation set up settlements on the West Bank?

7 Which banknotes were new but smaller in 1977?

8 What did British police use for the first time?

9 What was Skytrain?

10 Which party leader planned a pact with Labour?

11 Which festivities began with a bonfire in Windsor?

12 In which Commonwealth country was the prime minister dismissed by the governor general in 1975?

13 Which comedian known for his cigar and bushy eyebrows also died that year?

14 Who became British ambassador to the USA?

15 Who was the ambassador's father-in-law?

●●●

ANSWERS

1, New York 2, Donna Summer 3, Star Wars 4, Steve Ovett 5, The Space Shuttle 6, Israel 7, Pound notes 8, Riot shields 9, A new trans-Atlantic airliner 10, David Steel 11, The Queen's Silver Jubilee 12, Australia 13, Groucho Marx 14, Peter Jay 15, James Callaghan, prime minister

QUIZ 218
SPORT

🟢🟢🟢🟢🟢🟢🟢🟢🟢🟢🟢🟢🟢🟢🟢🟢🟢🟢🟢🟢🟢🟢🟢🟢🟢🟢🟢🟢🟢🟢🟢🟢🟢🟢🟢🟢🟢🟢🟢

1 Who won his third world snooker title in 1977?

2 For which country was Sid Going an international?

3 And what game did he play?

4 For which Rugby League club did Mick Burke kick 140 goals in 1978–79?

5 And which cup did they win in 1979?

6 At what weight did boxer Michael Spinks win Olympic gold in 1976?

7 Who captained Brazil in the 1970 World Cup final?

8 How many internationals were in Sunderland's 1973 FA Cup final team?

9 Which future TV presenter signed pro for Leicester City in 1978?

10 Which county did Norman Gifford play cricket for from 1971–80?

11 Which county never won a match in the 1979 cricket season?

12 Which middleweight boxer won a Lonsdale belt in 1975?

13 In which country was Joe Bugner born?

14 Who captained Ipswich Town in the 1978 FA Cup final?

15 Who was Ipswich's manager?

🟢🟢🟢🟢🟢🟢🟢🟢🟢🟢🟢🟢🟢🟢🟢🟢🟢🟢🟢🟢🟢🟢🟢🟢🟢🟢🟢🟢🟢🟢🟢🟢🟢🟢🟢🟢🟢🟢🟢

ANSWERS

1, John Spencer 2, New Zealand 3, Rugby union 4, Widnes 5, The Challenge Cup 6, Middlweight 7, Carlos Alberto 8, None 9, Gary Lineker 10, Worcestershire 11, Glamorgan 12, Chris Finnegan 13, Hungary 14, Mick Mills 15, Bobby Robson

QUIZ 219
WORLD EVENTS
1974

1. Which heiress was abducted in San Francisco?
2. What speed limit was in force on Britain's motorways?
3. Who was ejected from the Northern Ireland assembly?
4. Where was Liam Cosgrave premier?
5. Who said he would quit as Archbishop of Canterbury?
6. Which royal family member escaped kidnap in The Mall?
7. Where did General Spinola take power in April?
8. Which Israeli party did Yitzak Rabin lead?
9. What happened to Rutland?
10. What did the initials SLA stand for in US revolutionary circles?
11. Which guide gave the thumbs-down to British restaurants?
12. Where did Helmut Schmidt gain the top job?
13. For what was Dr Bridget Dugdale jailed?
14. Which royal duke died in June?
15. Who won the French presidential election?

ANSWERS

1, Patty Hearst 2, 50 mph 3, Ian Paisley 4, The Irish Republic 5, Michael Ramsey 6, Princess Anne 7, Portugal 8, Labour 9, It disappeared after local government changes 10, Symbionese Liberation Army 11 The Michelin 12, West Germany 13, Art theft 14, The Duke of Gloucester 15, Valery Giscard d'Estaing

QUIZ 220
SPORT

Name the soccer clubs for which these pairs played together

1 Keegan and Toshack

2 Buchan and Macari

3 Osgood and Cooke

4 Moore and Mullery

5 Chivers and Peters

6 Hughes and Hall

7 Labone and Harvey

8 Simpson and Armstrong

9 Bonds and Taylor

10 Macdonald and Tudor

11 McGovern and O'Hare

12 Bell and Lee

13 Wilson and McLintock

14 Brown and Astle

15 Giles and Lorimer

ANSWERS

1. Liverpool 2. Manchester United 3. Chelsea 4. Fulham 5. Spurs 6. Liverpool 7. Everton 8. Arsenal 9. West Ham 10. Newcastle 11. Derby 12. Manchester City 13. Arsenal 14. West Bromwich Albion 15. Leeds

QUIZ 221
PEOPLE

1 Which actress played poet Stevie Smith on stage in 1977?

2 In which play did Joan Hickson eat pilchards in bed?

3 Whose party was a stage hit in 1977?

4 Who bought Warwick Castle in 1978?

5 Who was *Cleopatra* in 1978?

6 Which Midlands town did Betty Boothroyd represent as MP from 1973?

7 Which famous Italian car designer died in 1975?

8 Who wrote a book called *Advice to a Young Scientist*?

9 Which American sexologists married in 1971?

10 In which country was Melina Mercouri an MP?

11 Who was called 'the angry man of jazz'?

12 Which Australian statesman died in 1978?

13 Who was Roberto Rossellini?

14 Was Mark Rothko a painter or a politician?

15 Who wrote a Book of *Boudoir Beauties* (1975)?

ANSWERS

1, Glenda Jackson 2, *Bedroom Farce* 3, *Abigail's Party* 4, Madame Tussaud's 5, Glenda Jackson 6, West Bromwich 7, Ernesto Maserati 8, Sir Peter Medawar 9, Masters and Johnson 10, Greece 11, Charles Mingus 12, Sir Robert Menzies 13, Italian film director, died 1977 14, A painter, died 1970 15, Ronnie Barker

SCIENCE & TECHNOLOGY

1 What was the BH-7 being tested by the Royal Navy in 1971?

2 Which transplant "first" was achieved in Munich in 1970: a) heart b) nerve or c) brain?

3 What in 1970 was extended to 12 months for cats and dogs in the UK?

4 Which very long-lived trees were being used by '70s archaeologists to aid dating?

5 Which drug caused birth defects for which 18 British children were awarded damages in 1970?

6 What was Cygnus 1, found in 1971?

7 What was the RB-211 being developed by Rolls-Royce?

8 Which major engineering project was completed in Egypt in 1970?

9 Which Communist country had helped build it?

10 Which ancient disease was worldwide in the early 70s, especially in Africa and India?

11 What was Prospero, a British first of 1971?

12 Was a "patch booster" designed to aid heart patients, improve rocket launches, or speed up telephone calls?

13 What did the initials GARP mean to weather scientists in the 70s?

14 The commander of the Apollo 14 Moon mission was a space veteran; who was he?

15 When had he first flown in space?

ANSWERS

1, A hovercraft 2, b) nerve 3, Quarantine period on entering the country 4, Bristlecone pines 5, Thalidomide 6, A star 7, An aircraft engine 8, The Aswan Dam 9, The USSR 10, Cholera 11, A space satellite 12, Aid heart patients (it was a mechanical pump attached to the aorta) 13, Global Atmospheric Research Programme 14, Alan Shepard 15, 1961

QUIZ 229
ARTS & ENTERTAINMENT

1 Who sang *Mama Weer All Crazee Now*?

2 Of which group had Allan Klein been manager before a falling-out?

3 Complete these bluesmen's names, all appearing in a 1972 festival: Muddy …

4 Howlin' …

5 Dr …

6 And complete this 1972 TV show title: *The Old Grey* …

7 Who released an album called *Glitter* in 1972?

8 Who wrote a song called *You're So Vain*?

9 Who stopped a Manfred Mann Earth Band concert in Miami University?

10 Why?

11 Another 70s name to complete. Mott the … ?

12 Whose 1972 single was called *Starman*?

13 Who sang *The First Time Ever I Saw Your Face*?

14 In which Clint Eastwood film did it feature?

15 And who sang *Rocket Man*?

ANSWERS

1, Slade 2, The Rolling Stones 3, Waters 4, Wolf 5, John 6, Whistle Test 7, Gary Glitter 8, Carly Simon 9, The police 10, Too noisy 11, Hoople 12, David Bowie 13, Roberta Flack 14, Play Misty for Me 15, Elton John

SPORT

1970 WORLD CUP

●●●

1 Where were the 1970 World Cup finals played?

2 Which two factors made the games testing for visiting players?

3 Who took over as Brazil's coach just before the tournament?

4 Whom did the local press call thieves and drunks?

5 Who was England's left back?

6 Which Spurs player wore the number four shirt for England?

7 For which team did Jairzinho play?

8 Who knocked out Mexico in the quarter finals?

9 Whose save was acclaimed as the save of the finals?

10 What kept him out of England's crucial match?

11 Who took his place?

12 What was the result of this key match?

13 Which England star was substituted controversially?

14 Which two teams met in the final?

15 And who won?

●●●

ANSWERS

1. Mexico 2. The altitude and the midday heat 3. Zagalo 4. England 5. Terry Cooper 6. Alan Mullery 7. Brazil 8. Italy 9. Gordon Banks' save from Pele 10. Illness 11. Peter Bonetti 12. West Germany beat England 3-2 13. Bobby Charlton 14. Brazil and Italy 15. Brazil won 4-1

PEOPLE

•••

Complete the names of these 70s people-in-the-news

1 Eddy, Belgian cyclist

2 Roy of the EEC

3 Jimmy of the tennis court

4 Paul who starred in The Sting

5 Gareth behind the scrum

6 John on ice

7 Tim the lyricist

8 Angela the newsreader

9 Viv the cricketer

10 David the swimming medallist

11 Jodie the young actress

12 Winnie the South African freedom fighter

13 Patti, heiress turned bank robber

14 Ray the England goalkeeper

15 Edward the prime ministerial sailor

•••

ANSWERS

1, Eddy Merckx 2, Jenkins 3, Connors 4, Newman 5, Edwards 6, Curry 7, Rice 8, Rippon 9, Richards 10, Wilkie 11, Foster 12, Mandela 13, Hearst 14, Clemence 15, Heath

QUIZ 226
POT LUCK

●●

1 How did Georgi Markov allegedly die in 1978?

2 Which award did Sir Nevill Mott win in 1977?

3 Which part of Britian was most affected by the disease?

4 In which year was the 200th Derby run?

5 Which horse was the winner?

6 Who played the part of Manuel in Fawlty Towers?

7 In this series, did Ballard Berkeley play an Admiral, a Major, or a Brigadier?

8 Was TriStar a new airliner, a cooker, or a TV set?

9 Which sports event move from White City to Crystal Palace in 1971?

10 In which sport did Howard and Rosemary Payne win international honours?

11 Was James Fisher, who died in 1970, a naturalist or Archbishop of Canterbury?

12 Who won a significant golf title at Chaska, Minnesota, in 1970?

13 What was different about golf balls after 1970?

14 Who was the novelist author of A Passage to India who died in 1970?

15 Was cricketer Mike Denness Scottish, Welsh or English?

●●

ANSWERS

14, E M Forster 15, A Scot
12, Tony Jacklin won the US Open 13, US and British balls were the same size
airliner 9, The AAA championships 10, They were both athletes 11, A naturalist
3, Southern England 4, 1979 5, Troy 6, Andrew Sachs 7, A Major 8, A new
1, Murdered by an umbrella-syringe containing poison 2, Nobel prize for Physics

QUIZ 227
SPORT
WORLD CUP 1974

1 Where were the 1974 World Cup finals played?

2 How many teams qualified from the British Isles?

3 For whom did Deyna play?

4 Which team's captain played for Leeds?

5 What was his name?

6 Who was said to run the West German team (not the manager)?

7 Who was the German manager?

8 For whom did Rensenbrinke play?

9 Of which team was Carlos Babington a member?

10 How many teams beat Scotland?

11 Which African team did the Scots beat 2-0?

12 For whom did Uli Hoeness play?

13 Who contested the final?

14 What was the score?

15 Who scored for the winners?

ANSWERS

1, West Germany 2, One (Scotland) 3, Poland 4, Scotland 5, Billy Bremner 6, Franz Beckenbauer 7, Helmut Schoen 8, Holland 9, Argentina 10, None 11, Zaire 12, West Germany 13, West Germany and Holland 14, 2-1 to West Gemany 15, Breitner (pen.) and Muller

WORLD EVENTS

1975

•••

1 For what did 67% vote 'yes' in Britain?

2 Which soccer star left Brazil for New York?

3 What went live on radio for the first time in Britain?

4 Who crashed trying to leap over 13 buses?

5 Which canal reopened after eight years?

6 Which ground staged the first ever World Cup cricket final?

7 Where was Dennis Hills jailed?

8 Who became Britain's Industry minister in June?

9 What was Deke Slayton doing in space?

10 Who was 'Dev', who died in August?

11 Where was Sheikh Mujibur Rahman shot dead?

12 Who was 'Carlos'?

13 What did Norton Villiers Triumph make?

14 Where was a terracotta army unearthed?

15 Which car company became government-owned?

•••

ANSWERS

1, Continued membership of the EEC. 2, Pele (who signed for Cosmos) 3, House of Commons proceedings 4, Evel Knievel. 5, The Suez Canal 6, Lord's 7, Uganda 8, Eric Varley 9, US astronaut aboard a joint US/Soviet mission 10, Eamon de Valera 11, Dacca, Bangladesh 12, A terrorist killer, allegedly working for the Palestinians 13, Motorbikes 14, China 15, British Leyland

PEOPLE

1 Who was Alberto Juantorena?

2 Did Bill Grundy interview on TV or play cricket for Yorkshire?

3 Who was *Rocky* on film?

4 Who had been married to Sir Max Mallowan?

5 Who directed the film *Taxi Driver*?

6 Who wrote *Dixon of Dock Green*?

7 She died in 1971; she was known for her showbiz partnership with Ben Lyon. Who was she?

8 Who starred with Jane Fonda in the film *Julia*?

9 Who played Edward in *Edward and Mrs Simpson*?

10 Where was General Omar Torriojos the army strongman in 1972?

11 Where did Scott and Irwin take a drive in 1971?

12 Who was Mrs Thatcher's first Foreign Secretary?

13 Which Hollywood sweetheart died in May 1979?

14 Who captained the 1971 British Lions?

15 Who was Alec Stock?

ANSWERS

1, A Cuban runner, world record holder at 800 metres. 2, TV interviewer (and journalist) 3, Sylvester Stallone 4, Agatha Christie 5, Martin Scorsese 6, Lord Ted Willis 7, Bebe Daniels 8, Vanessa Redgrave 9, Edward Fox 10, Panama 11, On the Moon (they were *Apollo 15* astronauts) 12, Lord Carrington 13, Mary Pickford 14, John Dawes 15, A soccer manager, who took Fulham to the 1975 FA Cup Final

WORLD EVENTS

1975

1 Which party leader was voted out by his own MPs?

2 How many children did his successor have?

3 Who was she?

4 Why were people in Luanda celebrating?

5 Where were the Khmer Rouge fighting?

6 What was the Imperial company to make no more of in Britain?

7 What cost £18 a year in Britain?

8 Who became the world's only Hindu king?

9 Of which country was Nikolai Bulganin an ex-leader?

10 Who was Susan Hayward, who died in March?

11 Which title did Anatoly Karpov win?

12 What were Michael Foot and Tony Benn campaigning against?

13 Where did President Thieu resign?

14 Which Chinese statesman died in April?

15 Where were 11 US marines the last to leave?

ANSWERS

1. Edward Heath 2. Two 3. Margaret Thatcher 4. Angola gained its independence 5. Cambodia 6. Typewriters 7. A colour TV licence 8. Birendra of Nepal 9. USSR 10. An American actress 11. World chess champion 12. Britain's membership of the EEC 13. South Vietnam 14. Chiang Kai-shek 15. The US embassy in Saigon

QUIZ 231
POT LUCK

•••

1 Which teams drew the 1970 FA Cup Final?

2 How many years had passed since the FA Cup final had last ended in a draw?

3 Who won the 1970 replay?

4 What year did China launch its first satellite?

5 Which country was expelled from the Olympic movement in 1970?

6 Which racehorse had to be put down in 1970 because it had arthritis?

7 What exotic animal was sighted in the River Ouse in 1970?

8 Which amateur team reached the 4th round of the FA Cup in 1970?

9 Who beat them?

10 Which sporting body gained a royal charter in 1970?

11 What was happening in Osaka, Japan, in 1970?

12 When Willy Brandt met Willi Stoph, which two countries did they represent?

13 Who commanded Apollo 13?

14 How were drawn European Cup soccer matches settled before 1970?

15 What new method for deciding such matches was introduced in 1970?

•••

ANSWERS

1. Leeds and Chelsea 2, 58 3, Chelsea won 2-1 4, 1970 5, South Africa 6, Arkle 7, A crocodile 8, Sutton United 9, Leeds, 6-0 10 The Jockey Club 11, Expo 70 12, West and East Germany 13, Frank Lovell 14, The toss of a coin 15, Penalty shoot-outs

ARTS & ENTERTAINMENT

Name the artist or the song for these more or less "one-hit wonders"

1 Art Garfunkel

2 *My Sweet Lord*

3 *No Charge*?

4 *Eye Level* – a hit for …?

5 Typically Tropical was their name, and their hit was …?

6 *No Charge* – who did well with this title?

7 *Matchstalk Men and Matchstalk Cats and Dogs* … who sang it?

8 Anita Ward: song title?

9 *Annie's Song*

10 *One Day At A Time*, a hit for … who?

11 Althia and Donna sang what in 1978?

12 *Float on*?

13 Seashells in 1972?

14 *Easy Easy* (1974); now who sang that …?

15 Minnie Riperton in 1975, remember the song?

ANSWERS

1, *Bright Eyes* 2, George Harrison 3, J J Barrie 4, The Simon Park Orchestra 5, *Barbados* 6, J J Barrie 7, Brian and Michael 8, *Ring My Bell* 9, John Denver 10, Lena Martell 11, *Up Town Top Ranking* 12, The Floaters 13, *Maybe I Know* 14, Scotland's World Cup squad 15, *Loving You*

PEOPLE

•••

1 Who was "Plum" who died in 1975?

2 Who wrote *The History Man*?

3 For which London soccer club did David O'Leary play?

4 Who starred in *One Flew Over The Cuckoo's Nest*?

5 Who starred in the sequel to *True Grit*?

6 What was the film called?

7 Which sculptress died in a fire at St Ives?

8 Who sang *Puppy Love*?

9 Which rock singer's real name was Vincent Furnier?

10 Which TV role did Jack Warner retire from?

11 Who was the first Russian man to reach the Wimbledon final (1973)?

12 Which evangelist went to South Korea in 1973?

13 Who became MP for Rochdale in 1972?

14 And which party did he represent?

15 Who was Margaret Bourke-White, who died in 1971?

•••

ANSWERS

1. P G Wodehouse 2. Malcolm Bradbury 3. Arsenal 4. Jack Nicholson 5. John Wayne 6. *Rooster Cogburn* 7. Barbara Hepworth 8. Donny Osmond 9. Alice Cooper 10. PC Dixon in *Dixon of Dock Green* 11. Alex Metreveli 12. Billy Graham 13. Cyril Smith 14. Liberal 15. An American photographer

QUIZ 294
POT LUCK

●●●

1 Who played Lord Byron in the film about Lady Caroline Lamb?

2 Which doctor had he played in a TV series?

3 Who played Chief Inspector Barlow in *Softly Softly*?

4 What was a Sinclair Executive?

5 Which car maker produced the Variant?

6 What did Hector Powe sell?

7 Who made a children's TV series about Sir Prancelot?

8 And with which pirate character was he more famously associated?

9 Who won the US Open tennis title in 1974?

10 Who shared the 1976 Nobel Peace Prize?

11 Where had the winners been active?

12 Was Gregory Corso a poet or a gangster?

13 In the *Bill Cosby Show*, did Bill play a teacher, a policeman, or a salesman?

14 Which letter-writer hosted *Masterpiece Theatre* on American TV?

15 Which German scientist had a comet named after him in 1973?

●●●

ANSWERS

1, Richard Chamberlain 2, *Dr Kildare* 3, Stratford Johns 4, A calculator 5, Volkswagen 6, Menswear 7, John Ryan 8, *Captain Pugwash* 9, Jimmy Connors 10, Mairead Corrigan and Betty Williams 11, Northern Ireland 12, A US poet 13, A teacher 14, Alistair Cooke 15, Dr Lubous Kohoutek

QUIZ 295
SCIENCE & TECHNOLOGY

1 Which company built its 100,000th aircraft in May 1972?

2 Which was Europe's first wide-body airliner?

3 What year was its maiden flight?

4 Which airliner completed 25 years of turboprop service in 1978?

5 What was the A-10A Thunderbolt designed to 'bust'?

6 Which consortium built the MRCA or Tornado?

7 What was the Soviet name for what NATO called the Foxbat?

8 By what name was the US Marines' AV-8A better known?

9 Which new British warship had a ski-ramp?

10 Which aircraft carried the Enterprise on its back in 1977?

11 What was the Gossamer Condor?

12 What was Solar One?

13 What did the initials ASTP stand for?

14 Which aircraft did Bryan Allen pedal across the Channel in 1979?

15 Did the flight take: a) 1 hour b) 2 hours 49 minutes or c) 3 hours 50 minutes?

ANSWERS

1. Cessna 2. The Airbus A300 3. 1972 4. The Vickers Viscount 5. Tanks 6. Panavia 7. The MiG-25 8. Harrier 9. The Harrier-carrier HMS Invincible 10. A modified Boeing 747 11. A man-powered aircraft 12. An electric aircraft 13. Apollo-Soyuz Test Project 14. The Gossamer Albatross 15. b) 2 hours 49 minutes

ARTS & ENTERTAINMENT

1 Who sang *Love Is The Drug*?

2 Which army band played *Amazing Grace* into the charts?

3 Who sang *Sugar Baby Love*?

4 Tom Petty and the … ?

5 *Another Brick in the Wall (part 2)* was a hit for which band?

6 Who had a hit with *Lady Eleanor* in 1972?

7 Laurie Lingo and the … who?

8 And their 1976 hit?

9 Which soccer team sang *We Can Do It* in 1977?

10 Who sang *Silver Star* in 1976?

11 Whose *Out of Time* was reissued in 1975?

12 Who sang *Sugar Me* in 1972?

13 And who sang *All Kinds of Everything* in 1970?

14 Who did what he did for *Maria* in 1971?

15 And was Candlewick Green a duo, a band, or a railway station?

ANSWERS

1. Roxy Music. 2. The Royal Scots Dragoon Guards (with pipes and drums) 3. The Rubettes 4. Heartbreakers 5. Pink Floyd 6. Lindisfarne 7. The Dipsticks 8. Convoy G.B. 9. Liverpool 10. Four Seasons 11. Chris Farlowe 12. Lynsey De Paul 13. Dana 14. Tony Christie (I Did What I Did For Maria) 15. A duo, with a minor hit in 1974

WORLD EVENTS

1975

••

1 Where were UNITA and MPLA at war?

2 Which desert colony did Morocco want from Spain?

3 Where was Sir John Kerr Governor-General?

4 Where did the Cortes swear in a new king?

5 Which organization kidnapped Tiede Herrema?

6 Where did prime minister Rashid Karami face a civil war in 1975?

7 What came ashore at Grangemouth for the first time?

8 Where did terrorists take over the Indonesian consulate?

9 What was Carlos doing in Vienna?

10 With what organization was Sheikh Yamani associated?

11 What nationality was he?

12 Where were John and Sheila Matthews held hostage?

13 Where is Dili, in the news in 1975 and in 1999?

14 Which political party did Malcolm Fraser lead?

15 With what crime was Gunther Guillaume of West Germany accused?

••

ANSWERS

1, Angola 2, Spanish Sahara 3, Australia 4, Spain 5, The IRA 6, Lebanon 7, North Sea oil 8, Amsterdam 9, Taking oil ministers hostage 10, OPEC 11, Saudi 12, Their flat in Balcombe Street 13, East Timor 14, Australian Liberal Party 15, Spying for East Germany

QUIZ 238
SPORT
WORLD CUP 1978

1 Where were the 1978 World Cup finals held?

2 Which Dutch star striker was absent?

3 And which German had gone to New York?

4 Which team did Bearzot manage?

5 Who was Scotland's manager?

6 Were England in the finals?

7 Which Celtic full back missed the finals through injury?

8 For whom did Dino Zoff keep goal?

9 Which team did Michel Platini play for?

10 Who beat Scotland in their first match?

11 Against whom did they then draw 1-1?

12 Which Scot was sent home for failing a drugs test?

13 Whose goal against Holland became a TV highlight?

14 Which teams met in the 1978 final?

15 What was the result?

ANSWERS

1, Argentina 2, Cruyff 3, Beckenbauer 4, Italy 5, Ally Macleod 6, No 7, Danny McGrain 8, Italy 9, France 10 Peru 3-1 11, Iran 12, Willie Johnston 13, Archie Gemmill's 14, Argentina and Holland 15, 3-1 to Argentina

QUIZ 239
ARTS & ENTERTAINMENT

1 With which band did Johnny Rotten sing?

2 Which group featured on a US compilation album called *Rock 'n' Roll Music*?

3 Who had a *Love Hangover*?

4 Who partnered Elton John on an August 76 hit?

5 And what was the song?

6 Which group played a 15th anniversary concert in the USA?

7 Where did Cliff Richard tour in August 1976?

8 Whose *Silly Love Songs* did well?

9 *Combine Harvester* was a hit for ... ?

10 What was the first number one of 1976?

11 Who sang *50 Ways To Leave Your Lover*?

12 Who sang *Save Your Kisses For Me*?

13 Who recorded a *Black and Blue* album?

14 Who got into drugs trouble in New York with Iggy Pop?

15 Who did Jimmy Carter say had inspired him musically?

ANSWERS

1. The Sex Pistols 2. The Beatles 3. Diana Ross 4. Kiki Dee 5. *Don't Go Breaking My Heart* 6. The Beach Boys 7. Russia 8. Wings 9. The Wurzels 10. *Bohemian Rhapsody by Queen* 11. Paul Simon 12. The Brotherhood of Man 13. The Rolling Stones 14. David Bowie 15. Bob Dylan, the Beatles and Led Zeppelin

QUIZ 240
POT LUCK

●●

1 Who wrote *The Female Eunuch*?

2 Who said "George, don't do that"?

3 Who built the Beta car?

4 What did the initials BSA mean to house-owners?

5 Where was Tun Abdul Razak leader?

6 Was Clay Reggazoni a) a racing driver, b) a boxer?

7 For which London soccer club did Stan Bowles play?

8 What sport did Vijay Amritaj play?

9 Who starred as "Harry O" on TV?

10 Who had friends called Teddy and Looby Loo?

11 Which TV game show did Eddie Waring co-present?

12 And on which sport did he commentate?

13 Which radio doctor later became boss of the BBC?

14 Where was Chou En-lai part of the government?

15 In which American city was The Trib newspaper launched in 1979?

●●

ANSWERS

1, Germaine Greer, 2, Joyce Grenfell 3, Lancia 4, Building Societies Association 5, Malaysia 6, a) racing driver 7, Queens Park Rangers 8, Tennis 9, David Janssen 10, Andy Pandy 11, It's A Knockout (Jeux Sans Frontieres) 12, Rugby League 13, Lord Hill of Luton (Charles Hill) 14, China 15, New York

QUIZ 241
WORLD EVENTS
1976

1 What mishap befell HMS *Andromeda*?

2 Who was attacked as 'the Iron Lady'?

3 And by which government?

4 Which Chinese leader died in January?

5 What post did George Thomas accept?

6 Where was Jonas Savimbi fighting a guerrilla war?

7 Where did the first British Airways Concorde touch down in January?

8 To which city did the Air France Concorde fly on its first trip?

9 Which Central American state was struck by an earthquake?

10 Who was chosen as the new Archbishop of Westminster?

11 Which aircraft company reportedly paid money to Prince Bernhardt of Holland?

12 Where was Dr Soares newly elected?

13 Where was the 'Green Line' breached?

14 Who ruled the Seychelles before 1976?

15 Where were Sabra and Chatilla?

ANSWERS

1, It was rammed by an Icelandic gunboat 2, Margaret Thatcher 3, The Soviet Union 4, Chou En-lai 5, Speaker of the House of Commons 6, Angola 7, Bahrain 8, Rio de Janeiro 9, Guatemala 10, Basil Hume 11, Lockheed 12, Portugal 13, Beirut 14, Britain 15, Lebanon

QUIZ 242
PEOPLE

🌑🌑🌑🌑🌑🌑🌑🌑🌑🌑🌑🌑🌑🌑🌑🌑🌑🌑🌑🌑🌑🌑🌑🌑🌑🌑🌑🌑🌑🌑

1 Who taught David Bowie how to mime?

2 Who played Barbara Good on TV?

3 Who directed the film *Akenfield* in 1974?

4 Which famous farceur (farce-actor) died in 1979?

5 Who wrote the novel *Heat and Dust*?

6 Which literary prize did it win in 1975?

7 Who wrote a TV play called *Beasts*?

8 Which more famous science fiction series did he create?

9 Who wrote The Case of *The Midwife Toad*?

10 In which country was this author born?

11 How did he and his wife die in 1983?

12 What was Humphrey Lyttelton's jazz instrument?

13 By what name did Frederick Bulsara find pop fame?

14 Which hit on which he sang became a soccer anthem?

15 Which Welsh-born actor played the father in Love Story (1970)?

🌑🌑🌑🌑🌑🌑🌑🌑🌑🌑🌑🌑🌑🌑🌑🌑🌑🌑🌑🌑🌑🌑🌑🌑🌑🌑🌑🌑🌑🌑

ANSWERS

1. Lindsay Kemp 2. Felicity Kendall 3. Peter Hall 4. Robertson Hare 5. Ruth Prawer Jhabvala 6. The Booker Prize 7. Nigel Kneale 8. *Quatermass* 9. Arthur Koestler 10. Hungary 11. They committed suicide 12. Trumpet 13. Freddie Mercury 14. Queen's *We Are The Champions* 15. Ray Milland

POT LUCK

1 By what name was murderer Donald Nielson known?

2 Who rode Empery to win the 1976 Derby?

3 What was Dame Sybil Thorndike noted as?

4 Which summer was Britain's hottest of the century?

5 Who was named 'Minister for Drought'?

6 Which thespian Alastair died in 1976?

7 Where was Charles de Gaulle airport opened?

8 Who captained Sunderland in the 1973 Cup Final?

9 Which island celebrated 1000 years of its Parliament in 1979?

10 What is the name of its Parliament?

11 How did 3 IRA prisoners escape from Mountjoy Prison in 1973?

12 Who wrote *Love in a Cold Climate*, and died in 1973?

13 Whose *Odessa File* became a best-seller?

14 Who played the professional killer in a film of another best-seller by this author?

15 Which 1975 TV series featured a space colony called Moonbase Alpha?

ANSWERS

1, The Black Panther. 2, Lester Piggot. 3, An actress. 4, 1976 5, Denis Howell 6, Alastair Sim. 7, Paris 8, Bobby Kerr 9, Isle of Man 10, The Tynwald 11, By helicopter 12, Nancy Mitford 13, Frederick Forsyth 14, Edward Fox 15, Space 1999

QUIZ 244
WORLD EVENTS
1976

● ●

1 Which famous politician wore Gannex raincoats?

2 Who received a life peerage for making them?

3 What job did Robert Mark hold?

4 Which counties agreed to stop feuding over fish?

5 Who was now too ill to see people visiting China?

6 Who was Britain's new prime minister?

7 Who was runner-up in the contest?

8 Where is Entebbe?

9 Whose commandos raided it in 1976?

10 Why did they do this?

11 To which airline did the airliner involved belong?

12 Why did people evacuate Seneso in Italy?

13 Where did Viking land on the Chryse plain?

14 Whom did the Democrats choose to run for President?

15 Which nation was celebrating its bicentennial?

● ●

ANSWERS

1, Harold Wilson 2, Joseph Kagan 3, Commissioner of the Metropolitan Police 4, Britain and Iceland 5, Mao-TSe-tung 6, James Callaghan 7, Michael Foot 8, Uganda 9, Israel's 10, The free hostages taken by pro-Palestinian hijackers 11, Air France 12, There was an escape of dangerous chemicals from a factory 13, Mars 14, Jimmy Carter 15, The USA

QUIZ 245
ARTS &
ENTERTAINMENT

. . . .

1 Who sang *Don't Give Up On Us*?

2 In which TV cops show had he starred?

3 Whose *Dancing Queen* was shooting high?

4 Paul Weller, Bruce Foxton and Rick Buckler made up … who?

5 Whose *Rumours* album was a hit this year?

6 Whose single was called *White Riot*?

7 *Less Than Zero* was the first hit for who?

8 Who sang *Angelo*?

9 Who sang *Looks Like We Made It*?

10 Who was *Free*?

11 Whose *God Save The Queen* was released in May 1977?

12 The singer in question one came back in the charts with a follow-up. Title?

13 Whose *2-4-6-8 Motorway* was a hit?

14 Which British rock star died in a September 1977 road crash?

15 And whose posthumous hit was a song called *Way Down*?

. . . .

ANSWERS

1, David Soul 2, *Starsky and Hutch* 3, ABBA 4, The Jam 5, Fleetwood Mac 6, The Clash 7, Elvis Costello 8, Brotherhood of Man 9, Barry Manilow 10, Deniece Williams 11, The Sex Pistols 12, *Silver Lady* 13, The Tom Robinson Band 14, Marc Bolan 15, Elvis Presley

QUIZ 246
PEOPLE

1 Which Scot became MP for Kingston upon Thames in 1972?

2 Whose car collection became the National Motor Museum?

3 Which English comic actor appeared in the film *10*?

4 Which astronomer wrote *A Guide To The Moon*?

5 Known as the "wee blue devil", this Scottish soccer star died in 1971. Name?

6 With which team was he associated?

7 Which once-disgraced minister received an OBE in 1975 for his charitable work?

8 Which comedienne appeared in a TV spy serial alongside "George Smiley"?

9 Was Alfred Deller (died 1979) a singer, a painter or a politician?

10 Who left the National Coal Board in 1971?

11 Who shared a 266-run partnership with Fletcher for England against New Zealand in the 1974-75 cricket series?

12 Whose autobiography was called *A Sense Of Freedom*?

13 Which clown retired from Blackpool Tower Circus in 1979?

14 Who made his last screen appearance in the series *QB VII* in 1974?

15 Who starred in *Up The Chastity Belt* (1972)?

ANSWERS

1, Norman Lamont 2, Lord Montague of Beaulieu 3, Dudley Moore 4, Patrick Moore 5, Alan Morton 6, Glasgow Rangers 7, John Profumo 8, Beryl Reid 9, A singer (counter-tenor) 10, Lord Robens 11, Mike Denness 12, Jimmy Boyle 13, Charlie Cairoli 14, Jack Hawkins 15, Frankie Howerd

QUIZ 247
POT LUCK

●●

1 What unusual arachnid turned up in a Reading laundry in 1974?

2 How much per pound did Golden Delicious apples cost in 1974?

3 What was the SR-71?

4 Which speed record did it break in 1974?

5 Which US company built it?

6 With which trade union was Joe Gormley associated?

7 In which country were 10 pop singers charged with lottery fraud in 1974?

8 Did 'boat people' come from Southeast Asia or South America?

9 Who created Ziggy Stardust?

10 Which popular poet made her name on TV's *Opportunity Knocks* in 1975?

11 He was Hamlet in 1975; later he played Gandhi. Name?

12 Was Magnus Pyke a scientist, travel show host, or TV cook?

13 Who wrote *I Can't Stay Long*?

14 Which Juliet joined the RSC in 1978?

15 Which 1970 film won John Mills an Oscar?

●●
ANSWERS

1, A scorpion 2, 10p 3, A US jet plane 4, Fastest trans-Atlantic crossing 5, Lockheed 6, NUM (National Union of Mineworkers) 7, Italy 8, Southeast Asia 9, David Bowie 10, Pam Ayres 11, Ben Kingsley 12, A scientist 13, Laurie Lee 14, Juliet Stevenson 15, Ryan's Daughter

QUIZ 240
POT LUCK

●●

1 Which punk band's 1978 US tour ended in the Winterland Theater in San Francisco?

2 What did the band's lead singer announce the following day?

3 What year was the first hit rap single in the USA?

4 In which country was the legal age for girls to marry reduced to 13 in 1979?

5 Who sang *Give Ireland Back to the Irish* in 1972?

6 What fish was caught in the Thames in 1974, after an absence of 140 years?

7 Was the 1972 film *Solaris* a science fiction movie or a Western?

8 Who played the title role in the 1971 film *Shaft*?

9 A song called *Hey Rock and Roll* started this band's career rolling in 1974; who were they?

10 Complete the singing partnership; Peters and …?

11 Which TV family lived at 165 Eaton Place?

12 Complete the title of this 1974 Bond film: *The Man With* …?

13 Who sang the title song from this film?

14 On which islands was TV's Bergerac series set?

15 Who played Bergerac?

●●

ANSWERS

1, The Sex Pistols 2, That the band was finished 3, 1979 4, Iran 5, Paul McCartney and Wings 6, A salmon 7, A science fiction movie 8, Richard Roundtree 9, Showaddywaddy 10, Lee 11, The Bellamys of *Upstairs, Downstairs* 12, the *Golden Gun* 13, Lulu 14, The Channel Islands 15, John Nettles

QUIZ 249
WORLD EVENTS
1976

1 Where did the socialists lose power after 30 years?

2 Which Chinese leader died on September 9?

3 For how long had he led China?

4 Who became Britain's Home Secretary in September?

5 Who announced that black majority rule would come after all?

6 And in which country?

7 Which London festivity was marred by violence?

8 Why was car-washing banned in much of Britain?

9 Where were the Soweto riots?

10 Where were the Gang of Four jailed?

11 Whose widow was among them?

12 Who was the architect of Britain's new National Theatre?

13 Which famous actor had an auditorium named after him?

14 Who got a second term as UN Secretary-General?

15 Who got a new job after a November election?

ANSWERS

1, Sweden 2, Mao-Tse-tung 3, Since 1949 4, Merlyn Rees 5, Ian Smith 6, Rhodesia 7, The Notting Hill Carnival 8, Because of the summer drought 9, South Africa 10, China 11, Mao's widow 12, Denys Lasdun 13, Olivier 14, Kurt Waldheim 15, Jimmy Carter, new US President

QUIZ 250
POT LUCK

●●

1 Which fictonal detective's "little grey cells" were laid to rest in 1976?

2 Whose husband was Prince Bernhard?

3 Who won gold on ice for Britain in 1976?

4 What did artist Carl André lay out in the Tate Gallery?

5 Which princess separated from her husband in 1976?

6 Which musician went to receive her OBE in a wheelchair?

7 Which crew won the 1976 Boat Race in record time?

8 Who hit 291 runs for West Indies against England that year?

9 Who was the newscaster who left ITN in 1979?

10 What nationality was runner Grete Waitz?

11 What did Godfrey Hounsfield invent?

12 What did Albino Cardinal Luciani become in 1978?

13 What was Double Eagle II?

14 And what first did it achieve in 1978?

15 What went on show in 1978, for the first time in 45 years?

●●

ANSWERS

1, Hercule Poirot, 2, Queen Juliana of the Netherlands 3, John Curry 4, Bricks 5, Princess Margaret, 6, Jacqueline Du Pré 7, Oxford 8, Viv Richards 9, Reginald Bosanquet 10, Norwegian 11, The CAT scanner 12, Pope 13, A balloon 14, It flew the Atlantic 15, The Turin Shroud

PEOPLE

1 Who sang *Lucille* in 1977?

2 Who were Barry, Maurice and Robin?

3 Who sang *Don't Cry for Me Argentina* to top the charts?

4 In which TV series had she appeared?

5 Where was Olivia Newton-John born?

6 Where did she grow up from the age of four?

7 With which group did Bob Geldof enter the 70s charts?

8 To which 'village' did the name Village People refer?

9 Who sang *Emma* in 1973?

10 Who was Leo Sayer's manager?

11 What outfit did Leo wear when he first hit the charts?

12 Whose 1976 Christmas song was *When a Child Is Born*?

13 What had previously been his best-known song?

14 Were Pussycat (1976) Dutch, American or British?

15 Whom had the Wurzels backed?

ANSWERS

1, Kenny Rogers 2, The Bee Gees 3, Julie Covington 4, *Rock Follies* 5, Cambridge, England 6, Australia 7, The Boomtown Rats 8, Greenwich Village 9, Hot Chocolate 10, Adam Faith 11, A clown's 12, Johnny Mathis 13, Misty 14, Dutch 15, Adge Cutler

QUIZ 252
SCIENCE & TECHNOLOGY

●●

1 What is Mox, first used in the 70s?

2 What kind of printer was new in 1975?

3 Which flower gave its name to another 70s printer?

4 What 'micro' gadget first appeared in 1971?

5 Which was the first planet to be landed on by a spacecraft?

6 Who launched the craft?

7 Which was the biggest orbital station at launch in 1973?

8 What was the first 'earth-resource' satellite?

9 Which rocket marked Europe's entry into space launching in 1979?

10 What kind of astronomy was the COS-B satellite designed for?

11 What was unusual about the Kulper Observatory?

12 What video system did Sony launch in 1975?

13 Who developed the rival system?

14 And what was it?

15 What was Selectavision?

●●

ANSWERS

1, A mixture of uranium and plutonium 2, Laser printer 3, Daisy wheel 4, Microprocessor 5, Venus 6, USSR 7, Skylab 8, Landsat 1 (1972) 9, Ariane 1 10, High energy gamma-ray studies 11 It was in a plane 12, Betamax 13, JVC 14, VHS 15, A video disc system from RCA (1974) later abandoned

QUIZ 259
ARTS &
ENTERTAINMENT

1. What new name did The Invaders (1979) later adopt?
2. Who sang *Y. M.C.A.*?
3. Who had a 1979 hit with *Heart of Glass*?
4. Where was The Star Club reopened?
5. Who were Prince Charles's favourite group in 1979?
6. Who set up Accomplice Records?
7. Who sang *I Will Survive*?
8. Who went *Walking on the Moon* in 1979?
9. Who sang *Video Killed the Radio Star*?
10. What was Cliff Richard's big 1979 hit?
11. *My Sharona* was a US hit for ... who?
12. Who made the *Regatta De Blanc* album?
13. *Laughter in the Rain* (1975) was a first hit single in 10 years for who?
14. Who hosted a revival of *Juke Box Jury* on TV?
15. And which DJ had presented the original version?

ANSWERS

1, Madness 2, Village People 3, Blondie 4, Hamburg 5, The Three Degrees 6, Bob Dylan 7, Gloria Gaynor 8, Police 9, Buggles 10, *We Don't Talk Anymore* 11, knack 12, Police 13, Neil Sedaka 14, Noel Edmunds 15, David Jacobs

POT LUCK

1 Which fast food chain was new in London in 1974?

2 Which Surrey town was hit by pub bombs in 1974?

3 Who played a child prostitute in the film *Taxi Driver*?

4 Who was named as the "fourth man" in British spy-circles?

5 Who was the girl in the *Not the Nine O'Clock News team*?

6 Who directed the film *Apocalypse Now*?

7 What sport did Phil Bennett play?

8 Which band had a 1972 hit with *All The Young Dudes*?

9 Which star had to pay "palimony" after a 1979 court case?

10 The author of *The Browning Version* died in 1977; who was he?

11 Which Labour MP crossed over to join the Conservatives?

12 In which sport was Niki Lauda a world champion?

13 What was Groucho Marx's first name?

14 For whom was Lady Armstrong-Jones a bridesmaid in 1973?

15 What did the French test at Mururoa Atoll?

ANSWERS

1, McDonald's 2, Guildford 3, Jodie Foster 4, Anthony Blunt 5, Pamela Stephenson 6, Francis Ford Coppola 7, Rugby union 8, Mott the Hoople 9, Lee Marvin 10, Sir Terence Rattigan 11, Reg Prentice 12, Motor racing 13, Julius 14, Princess Anne 15, H-bombs

PEOPLE

●●●

1 Hollywood actress, died 1977, born Lucille Le Suer. Who was she?

2 Who was US PGA champion in 1977?

3 Wife's name Oona, died in Switzerland; who was he?

4 Which former US vice-president and presidential candidate died this year?

5 Whose widow had a painting of her husband burned (it was revealed after she died)

6 Who painted the picture the couple disliked so much?

7 What did Ronnie Peterson do in the sporting world?

8 Was Willie John McBride an Irish rugby player or a Scottish soccer star?

9 Who called the 70s the 'Me' decade: a) Tom Wolfe b) Margaret Thatcher or c) Muhammad Ali?

10 With whom did Sid Vicious play and sing?

11 Which former Italian prime minister was kidnapped in 1977?

12 Which prison did Clint Eastwood plan to escape from in a 1979 film?

13 In which film was the villain called Hugo Drax?

14 And who played the hero in this film?

15 Of which country did Joe Clark become prime minister in 1979?

●●●

ANSWERS

1, Joan Crawford 2, Lanny Wadkins 3, Sir Charles Chaplin 4, Hubert Humphrey 5, Sir Winston Churchill's 6, Graham Sutherland 7, Grand Prix racing driver 8, Irish rugby player 9, a) Tom Wolfe (US writer) 10, The Sex Pistols 11, Aldo Moro 12, Alcatraz 13, Moonraker 14, Roger Moore (as 007) 15, Canada

QUIZ 256
POT LUCK

1 What were the first names of Rigsby's tenants in a popular TV sitcom?

2 What was the name of the show?

3 Which famous actor presented a TV show called *Sinister Tales*?

4 What could Britons get free on the NHS from 1974?

5 To which country did Mario Soares return from exile in 1974?

6 For whom did Norman Hunter play soccer?

7 Where was Ronald Biggs arrested in 1974?

8 With which 60s crime was he implicated?

9 Who sang *Devil Gate Drive*?

10 What time did British TV close down during the winter of 1973–74?

11 And why?

12 Where was Eric Gairy prime minister in 1974?

13 Who rode Columbus to success at Badminton?

14 Who sang *Chanson D'Amour*?

15 Who became US President in 1977?

ANSWERS

1, Alan, Philip and Ruth, 2, *Rising Damp* 3, Orson Welles 4, Family planning 5, Portugal 6, Leeds United 7, Brazil 8, The Great Train Robbery 9, Suzi Quatro 10, 10.30 pm 11, To save power during the 3-day week energy crisis 12, Grenada 13, Captain Mark Phillips 14, Manhattan Transfer 15, Jimmy Carter

QUIZ 257
SPORT
MOTOR RACING

1   Where was the Osterreichring circuit?

2   Which British driver died in a crash at the Dutch Grand Prix?

3   Which Swedish driver appeared for the first time in 1970?

4   Which team made its debut in 1973?

5   Which Grand Prix in 1972 was held at Mosport Park?

6   Who won his first world title in 1975?

7   What car was he driving?

8   Who won the last Grand Prix of the 1970s?

9   Where was the 1976 Grand Prix (West) held?

10 What nationality was Jackie Ickx?

11 Who won the 1978 driver's world title?

12 What nationality was he?

13 What car was he driving?

14 What nationality was driver Denny Hulme?

15 Who became the youngest-ever world champion in 1972?

ANSWERS

1, Austria 2, Piers Courage 3, Ronnie Peterson 4, Hesketh 5, Canadian 6, Niki Lauda 7, Ferrari 8, Gilles Villeneuve (Canada) 9, Long Beach, California 10, Belgian 11, Mario Andretti 12, American 13, Lotus-Ford 14, New Zealander 15, Emerson Fittipaldi!

QUIZ 258
WORLD EVENTS
1976

••

1 Which German terrorist was found dead in prison?

2 Which European-built airline type was making news with two hijacks this year?

3 Where was President Assad in power?

4 Into which country was he sending 'peace-keeping' troops?

5 In which political party was John Pardoe running for the leadership?

6 Where was former prime minister Tanaka arrested?

7 What was and is the IMF?

8 Which country borrowed as much as it could to boost its currency in September?

9 About which canal did the US government agree to new treaty talks?

10 Who went from Plains, Georgia to Washington?

11 Who opened the 1976 Olympic Games?

12 Which country provided the Games' outstanding gymnast?

13 Who was she?

14 In which post did Roy Mason succeed Merlyn Rees in 1976?

15 Which gymnast achieved the first perfect score of ten in Olympic history?

••

ANSWERS

1. Ulrike Meinhof 2, Airbus 3, Syria 4, Lebanon 5, Liberal Party in Britain 6, Japan 7, The International Monetary Fund 8, Britain 9, The Panama Canal 10, Jimmy Carter 11, The Queen 12, Romania 13, Nadia Comaneci 14, Northern Ireland Secretary 15, Nadia Comaneci

PEOPLE

Complete the showbiz names

1 Peters and …

2 Paper …

3 Francis … of Status Quo

4 … and Wise

5 Peter … and Dudley …

6 Tammy …

7 Brotherhood of …

8 Michael … chat show host

9 Manhattan …

10 David … of TV's *The Partridge Family*

11 Julie … starred in the film *The Go-Between*

12 Noele … of *Crossroads*

13 Denny … of Wings

14 Esther … of *The Big Time*

15 who married Desmond … in 1977

ANSWERS

QUIZ 260
WORLD EVENTS
1977

1 Which African state saw an emperor crowned?

2 Who was the new emperor?

3 Who died in his police cell in Port Elizabeth?

4 From where were boat people fleeing?

5 Who became Mayor of Paris?

6 Where did Charter 77 oppose the government?

7 Which widow of a famous prime minister died in December?

8 Which leaders met to try to bring Middle East peace?

9 Who became Israel's leader in April?

10 Which Indian leader was charged with corruption?

11 Who in South Africa was banned from meeting more than one person at a time?

12 Where was Benigno Aquino sentenced to death?

13 Which country had Kurt von Schusnigg, who died in 1977, led in the1930s?

14 Where was the Rev. Sithole in the news?

15 Where did a German airliner end up after a 'skyjack' in October?

ANSWERS

1, The Central African Republic (became an empire) 2, Jean-Bedel Bokassa 3, Steve Biko 4, South Vietnam 5, Jacques Chirac 6, Czechoslovakia 7, Lady Churchill 8, Begin of Israel and Sadat of Egypt 9, Shimon Peres 10, Mrs Gandhi 11, Newspaper editor Donald Woods 12, The Philippines 13, Austria 14, Rhodesia 15, Mogadishu, Somalia

QUIZ 261
POT LUCK

1 Where were the initials UVF familiar?

2 And what did they stand for?

3 Who wrote the play *Bedroom Farce*?

4 Complete the pop pairings: Daryl Hall and …?

5 Did Mrs Gandhi win or lose the 1977 election in India?

6 Where in Europe were free elections held in 1977 for the first time since the 1930s?

7 Complete the film title (1977): *Smokey and …*?

8 Who was the star of the film?

9 Which animals feature in the play *Equus*?

10 Who wrote the play?

11 At which game did Nigel Short excell?

12 What kind of fighting was Carl Douglas singing about in 1974?

13 Who were the royal wedding stars in Britain in 1973?

14 Who was Peter Niesewand?

15 What was the Vanguard?

ANSWERS

15, It was a British turboprop airliner
journalist, jailed in 1973 under the Official Secrets Act, and then released
11, Chess 12, Kung-fu 13, Princess Anne and Mark Phillips 14, A Rhodesian
5, She lost 6, Spain 7, The Bandit 8, Burt Reynolds 9, Horses 10, Peter Shaffer
1, Northern Ireland 2, Ulster Volunteer Force 3, Alan Ayckbourne 4, John Oates

QUIZ 262
ARTS & ENTERTAINMENT

1 What year were the Sex Pistols formed?

2 Whose children were called Dweezil and Moon Unit?

3 Captain Beefheart and … which band?

4 Who sang *Power to the People*?

5 Who made an album called *Surf's Up*?

6 Which group might have been called Turpentine (but decided against it)?

7 Where did Jim Morrison die?

8 What song won the 1974 Eurovision Song Contest?

9 To what film was *Stardust* a follow-up?

10 Who appeared as the Acid Queen in the film of *Tommy*?

11 Who sang *Love Will Keep Us Together*?

12 What was C W McCall's 1975 hit?

13 Who left the Faces to go solo in 1975?

14 In which city was Bob Marley's *No Woman No Cry* recorded?

15 Who had a son called Sean in October 1975?

ANSWERS

1, 1975 2, Frank Zappa's 3, The Magic Band 4, John Lennon 5, The Beach Boys 6, Wings 7, Paris 8, Waterloo 9, That'll Be The Day 10, Tina Turner 11, Captain and Tennille 12, Convoy 13, Rod Stewart 14, London 15, John Lennon and Yoko Ono

PEOPLE

- **1** Of which company did Michael Edwardes become boss in 1977?
- **2** Which royal had a baby in November this year?
- **3** Who sang *Wuthering Heights* in 1978?
- **4** Which British record producer died in 1979?
- **5** Who partnered John Travolta on the 1978 hit *Summer Nights*?
- **6** Was Tony Currie a footballer, a pop star or a union boss?
- **7** In which country was Prince Sihanouk a leader?
- **8** Which cricket commentator helped broadcast the queen's silver jubilee?
- **9** Who played Sergeant Wilson in *Dad's Army*?
- **10** Who wrote *The Sea, The Sea*?
- **11** Who began presenting *That's Life* in 1973?
- **12** Which financier switched to writing children's books?
- **13** Who became director of the Centre for Policy Studies in 1979?
- **14** Which organization did Vic Feather lead?
- **15** In which language did Isaac Bashevis Singer write?

ANSWERS

1, British Leyland, 2, Princess Anne 3, Kate Bush 4, Norrie Paramor 5, Olivia Newton-John 6, A footballer 7, Cambodia 8, Brian Johnston 9, John Le Mesurier 10, Iris Murdoch 11, Esther Rantzen 12, Jim Slater 13, David Young 14, The Trades Union Congress 15, Yiddish

POT LUCK

•••

1 Of which newspaper did Derek Jameson become editor in 1977?

2 Who had a radio show called *A Taste of Hunni*?

3 Whose Life did the Pythons film in 1979?

4 Who took the Midnight Train to Georgia in 1976?

5 What is Kenneth Clarke's middle name?

6 In whose government did he first gain office?

7 Which Joey rode the TT races?

8 Who wrote *Darkness Visible* (1979)?

9 Who rode Troy to win the 1979 Derby?

10 Which trans-Atlantic aviator died in 1974?

11 Which London street made the news in a 1975 siege?

12 Where is the Forties field?

13 Whose brother was Peter Fleming, who died in 1971?

14 Which famous snooker player died in 1978?

15 Who introduced a TV series called *The Magic of Dance*?

•••

ANSWERS

1. Daily Express 2. Gloria Hunniford 3. Brian's 4. Gladys Knight and the Pips 5. Harry 6. Edward Heath's 7. Joey Dunlop 8. William Golding 9. Willie Carson 10. Charles Lindbergh 11. Balcombe Street 12. The North Sea 13. Ian Fleming's 14. Joe Davis 15. Margot Fonteyn

QUIZ 265
SCIENCE & TECHNOLOGY

1 What happened to the *Europa 2* rocket in 1971?

2 Where was it launched?

3 Which rocket provided the first stage booster?

4 Where did the US carry out an underground nuclear test in 1971?

5 Which country soft-landed a probe on Mars in December 1971?

6 Which design of bridge caused concern after several collapsed in the early 1970s?

7 Which nation had scientists on board North Pole 16, a floating ice station?

8 What was BACCHUS?

9 What was the Glomar Challenger exploring in 1971? a) the sea b) space or c) the atmosphere?

10 What did DSRVs do?

11 Was Georgi Dobrovolski a cosmonaut, an atom scientist or Russia's science minister?

12 Where was Fra Mauro?

13 What was the name of the *Apollo 14* lunar module?

14 The *Viking 1* probe transmitted the first pictures from which planet?

15 What was the name of the Soviet Moon-crawler which 'died' in 1971?

ANSWERS

1. It blew up 2. French Guiana 3. Blue Streak 4. The Aleutian Islands 5. USSR 6. Box-girder bridges 7. Soviet Union 8. An underwater habitat for divers 9. a) the sea 10. They dived, DSRV= Deep Sea Research Vehicle 11. He was a cosmonaut 12. On the Moon 13. Antares 14. Mars 15. Lunokhod 1

QUIZ 266
ARTS &
ENTERTAINMENT

1 Whose 1970 new play lasted one minute?

2 Who wrote the *History of Western Philosophy*?

3 Which book sold a million copies in its first day?

4 For which musical skill did John Lill win a 1970 award in Moscow?

5 Was Dame Laura Knight (died 1970) a musician or painter?

6 How did Jimi Hendrix die in 1970?

7 What nationality was author Erich Maria Remarque (died 1970)?

8 Whose *Selected Poems* went on sale in 1970?

9 Which female singer died in 1970, of the same cause as Jimi Hendrix?

10 Who wrote about Lewis Eliot in a series of novels?

11 Which choreographer retired from the Royal Ballet in 1970?

12 With which orchestra was Sir John Barbirolli (died 1970) associated?

13 Which ITV sports programme was challenging the BBC's *Grandstand*?

14 Who played Shylock for the National Theatre in 1970?

15 Whose flying was cancelled by the demolition of the Scala Theatre in London?

ANSWERS

1 Why was Gary Gilmore in the news?

2 Where did Archbishop Luwum disappear?

3 Whose foreign minister was Yigal Allon?

4 What did the Vatican want stopped in church?

5 In which church did the Queen and Prince Philip attend a thanksgiving service for the Queen's jubilee in 1977?

6 Where did two 747 jets collide in March?

7 Where was Sadat talking tough?

8 Where was Shaba province?

9 Which 'hardliner' took over in Israel?

10 Where was James Mancham deposed?

11 Which high-profile Canadian couple parted?

12 Where did Jack Lynch win an election?

13 Where was Podgorny sacked as President?

14 Who was Pakistan's new strongman?

15 Who tried to bring about a 'social contract' with trade unions?

ANSWERS

1, He was the first person to be executed in the USA since the 1960s 2, Uganda 3, Israel's 4, The Latin Mass 5, St Paul's Cathedral 6, The Canary Islands 7, Egypt 8, Zaïre 9, Menachem Begin 10, Seychelles 11, Pierre and Margaret Trudeau 12, Irish Republic 13, USSR 14, General Zia ul-Haq 15, The British government

QUIZ 268
POT LUCK
1977

1. Which 11-year-old was a chess prodigy in 1977?
2. Who signed up 35 of the best for a rebel series?
3. Who became European Cup champions this year?
4. Whom did they beat?
5. Why were there beacons on hilltops in June?
6. Who won his 8th Derby on The Minstrel?
7. Whose killer broke jail in the USA?
8. Who, in 1977, sang *We're All Alone*?
9. What in 1977 did doctors say could shorten a person's life by about 5 minutes?
10. Who refused to be a Companion of Honour?
11. Who beat Sue Barker to foil hopes of an all-British Wimbledon ladies final?
12. Which American teenager was on his way to ride racehorses in Europe?
13. What cost £21 a year in Britain from August?
14. Which Cypriot leader died suddenly?
15. What came back safely from its first flight?

ANSWERS

1, Nigel Short 2, Kerry Packer (cricket) 3, Liverpool 4, Borussia Moenchengladbach 3-1 5, To begin celebrations for the Queen's jubilee 6, Lester Piggott 7, Martin Luther King's (James Earl Ray) 8, Rita Coolidge 9, Smoking a cigarette 10, Artist Francis Bacon 11, Betty Stove 12, Steve Cauthen 13, A colour TV licence 14, Archbishop Makarios 15, The Space Shuttle

QUIZ 269
ARTS & ENTERTAINMENT

1. For which film did Gene Hackman win the 1971 best actor Oscar?

2. Who was the film's director, also an Oscar-winner?

3. Who directed *Annie Hall* (1977)?

4. In which 1972 musical did Joel Grey star?

5. Who won successive Oscars as best supporting actor in 1976 and 1977?

6. Which actress won an award for *Julia* (1977)?

7. And which actress took away a statuette for *Kramer vs Kramer*?

8. Who won best actor award for the same film?

9. Who directed *The Sting*?

10. Who were the co-stars of that film?

11. Who played the victim of their 'sting'?

12. Who won a best-actress Oscar for *Coming Home* (1978)

13. Who got an Oscar for her role in *Norma Rae* (1979)?

14. In which film did Jack Nicholson win his 1975 best actor Oscar?

15. And which film gave Marlon Brando his 1972 Oscar?

ANSWERS

1, *The French Connection* 2, William Friedkin 3, Woody Allen 4, *Cabaret* 5, Jason Robards 6, Vanessa Redgrave 7, Meryl Streep 8, Dustin Hoffman 9, George Roy Hill 10, Robert Redford and Paul Newman 11, Robert Shaw 12, Jane Fonda 13, Sally Field 14, *One Flew Over the Cuckoo's Nest* 15, *The Godfather*

QUIZ 270
POT LUCK

●●●

1 For which film did Peter Finch win a posthumous Oscar?

2 Who was the first female Lord Warden of the Cinque Ports?

3 With which city's Playhouse was Richard Eyre associated?

4 Was Hans Eysenck a psychologist or a Dutch soccer star?

5 In what industry did Derek Ezra work?

6 The Queen's Silver Jubilee was in which year?

7 Of which jet airliner was the Nimrod a development?

8 In which year was Britain's biggest-ever teacher's strike?

9 Who recorded *In the Summertime*?

10 Why did the RAF shadow Bears?

11 What did Tektite 2 investigate?

12 Did Clarice Cliff design shoes or pottery?

13 What instrument did George Chisholm play?

14 Which northeast soccer club did Jack Charlton manage?

15 Who wrote In *Patagonia*?

●●●

ANSWERS

1, *Network* 2, The Queen Mother 3, Nottingham 4, A psychologist 5, Coal, as Chairman of the National Coal Board 6, 1977 7, Comet 8, 1970 9, Mungo Jerry 10, Bears were Nato-code named Soviet aircraft 11, The sea bed 12, Pottery 13, Trombone 14, Middlesborough 15, Bruce Chatwin

QUIZ 271
WORLD EVENTS
1978

1 Where was Qum the scene of anti-government riots?

2 Against whom was the rioters' anger chiefly directed?

3 Which ship were French helicopters trying to sink in the English Channel in 1978?

4 Where was Aldo Moro kidnapped?

5 Who claimed responsibility for the crime?

6 What happened to Moro?

7 What had the government refused to do?

8 Who would get control of their canal in 1999, according to a treaty?

9 What was the name of the oil tanker wrecked in the English Channel?

10 Where did Raymond Barre head a new government?

11 Where is Kabul, scene of fighting in a coup?

12 Where did protesters fight police over a planned new airport?

13 Why were Kenyans in mourning in August?

14 Where were Scharansky and Ginsburg on trial?

15 To which country did China cut off aid?

ANSWERS

QUIZ 272
PEOPLE

Complete the names

1 South African black leader Steve
2 Rotund Liberal Cyril
3 Liverpool "hard man" Tommy
4 Cricket rebel Tony
5 Defeated presidential runner George
6 Prime ministerial adviser Marcia
7 Israeli statesman David
8 Nobel prizewinner for medicine (1973) Nikolas
9 Comedian Benny
10 Gilbert who sang to Clair
11 John who played cop Regan
12 Ray who sang The Streak
13 French singer Charles
14 Footballer Allan nicknamed "Sniffer"
15 Soccer manager Brian of Derby and Nottingham Forest fame

ANSWERS

1.Biko 2. Smith 3, Smith 4, Greig 5, McGovern 6, Williams (Lady Falkender) 7, Ben Gurion 8, Tinbergen 9, Hill 10, O'Sullivan 11, Thaw 12, Stevens 13, Aznavour 14, Clarke 15, Clough

QUIZ 279
POT LUCK

•••

1 Who was charged with killing his girl friend Nancy Spungen?

2 Where was the arrest?

3 What happened to the charged person thereafter?

4 Who beat Korchoi at the board?

5 Who led a band called the New Barbarians in 1979?

6 Who was Zenon de Fleur Heirowski?

7 Whose husband was Stringer Davis, who died in 1973?

8 Who became Britain's Astronomer Royal?

9 Who became MP for Blaby in 1974?

10 What were the Monty Python team searching for on film in 1974?

11 For whom did Joe Corrigan play football?

12 Who presented the TV series *The Body in Question*?

13 Who won the European middle weight boxing title in 1977?

14 Who wrote *How to Cheat at Cooking*?

15 In which newspaper did Marc's cartoons appear?

•••

ANSWERS

1, Sid Vicious 2, New York 3, He was freed on bail and died from a heroin overdose in February 1979 4, Anatoly Karpov, world chess champion, 1978 5, Keith Richard 6, A guitarist with the UK rock band the Count Bishops 7, Margaret Rutherford's 8, Martin Ryle 9, Nigel Lawson 10, *The Holy Grail* 11, Manchester City 12, Jonathan Miller 13, Alan Minter 14, Delia Smith 15, *The Times*

QUIZ 274
WORLD EVENTS
1978

1. What caused an explosion at a Spanish campsite in July?
2. Into what was the Bingham inquiry looking?
3. Which car company bought Chrysler Europe?
4. How did Pope Paul VI die?
5. What was the Queen opening in Edmonton in August?
6. Which trio of leaders met at Camp David?
7. What agreement did they reach?
8. Where was Joshua Nkomo a nationalist leader?
9. Where were the Sandinistas gaining strength?
10. PW Botha was which country's new prime minister?
11. What did the initials in his name stand for?
12. Whose attempts to 'Westernize' his country sparked religious revolts?
13. Who owned the *Rainbow Warrior*?
14. Who tried to take over a chunk of Tanzania?
15. In which country did 900 members of an American cult kill themselves?

ANSWERS

1, A liquid gas tanker. 2, Allegations of 'sanctions-busting' oil deals with Rhodesia 3, Peugeot-Citroen 4, He had a heart attack 5, The Commonwealth Games 6, President Carter, Anwar Sadat and Menachem Begin 7, A peace treaty between Egypt and Israel 8, Rhodesia 9, Nicaragua 10, South Africa 11, Pieter Willem 12, The Shah of Iran 13, Greenpeace 14, Idi Amin of Uganda 15, Guyana

ART &
ENTERTAINMENT

Name the groups who performed these titles

1 *So You Win Again*

2 *Yes Sir I Can Boogie*

3 *Figaro*

4 *Puppy Love*

5 *Are 'Friends' Electric*

6 *Knock Three Times*

7 *Get It On*

8 *Cum On Feel The Noize*

9 *Love Me For A Reason*

10 *Down Down*

11 *Give A Little Love*

12 *If You Leave me Now*

13 *Night Fever*

14 *Welcome Home*

15 *When I Need You*

ANSWERS

1. Hot Chocolate 2. Baccara 3. Brotherhood of Man 4. Donny Osmond
5. Tubeway Army 6. Dawn 7. T Rex 8. Slade 9. Osmonds 10. Status Quo 11. Bay
City Rollers 12. Chicago 13. Bee Gees 14. Peters and Lee 15. Leo Sayer

PEOPLE

1 Which British athlete had a stadium in Belfast named after her?

2 Who wrote the 1975 play *Hitting Town*?

3 Who wrote about the Garnett family?

4 What 1973 book did he write, giving the view of the leading character?

5 On which sport was Bill McLaren airing his views?

6 Who wrote the western thriller *Breakheart Pass*?

7 Who was the most famous Barry in Wales?

8 To whom was novelist Pamela Hansford Johnson married?

9 Who wrote *The Plague Dogs*?

10 And who wrote *The Hand-Reared Boy*?

11 For which county did Denis Amiss play cricket?

12 Who made the film *Deliverance* (1972)?

13 Which Spanish painter celebrated his 90th birthday in 1971?

14 What is Ian Botham's middle name?

15 And with which county did he make his name in the 70s?

ANSWERS

1, Mary Peters 2, Stephen Poliakoff 3, Johnny Speight 4, The Thoughts of Chairman Alf 5, Rugby union 6, Alistair Maclean 7, Barry John 8, C P Snow 9, Richard Adams 10, Brian Aldiss 11, Warwickshire 12, John Boorman 13, Pablo Picasso 14, Terence 15, Somerset

POT LUCK

1971–72

1 In what year was *Amazing Grace* a hit?

2 Of which soccer club was Tommy Docherty made manager in December 1972?

3 Who starred in *Everything You Always Wanted to Know About Sex*?

4 Who became Poet Laureate in 1972?

5 Which character had the best songs (said some) in *Jesus Christ Superstar*?

6 Who succeeded King Frederick IX of Denmark?

7 Who made the film *Chelsea Girls*?

8 How old was Khrushchev when he died in 1971?

9 Were micro-skirts longer or shorter than mini-skirts?

10 Who rode a horse called Doublet?

11 Who was the loser in the 1971 Wimbledon ladies tennis singles final?

12 To whose family did Patricia Krenwinkel and Susan Atkins belong?

13 Who was Marianne Moore, who died in 1972?

14 Which former British monarch died in 1972?

15 In which city was this person living?

ANSWERS

1, 1972 2, Manchester United 3, Woody Allen 4, John Betjeman 5, Judas Iscariot 6, Queen Margrethe 7, Andy Warhol 8, 77 9, Shorter 10, Princess Anne 11, Margaret Court 12, Charles Manson's 13, An American poet 14, The Duke of Windsor 15, Paris

POT LUCK

●●

1 What was tied around the old oak tree (1973)?

2 Which railway station might have inspired ABBA's first hit?

3 When were Mud lonely in 1974?

4 What was Billy Connolly seeking in 1975?

5 What were these 1978 men, cats and dogs made of?

6 What were Police walking on in 1979?

7 What did Ian Dury suggest you hit him with?

8 Which river provided a 1976 hit for Pussycat?

9 Under what were Showaddywaddy the same year?

10 Which month was a February 1975 hit for Pilot?

11 Whom did Tammy Wynette tell us to stand by?

12 What was Mouldy in 1972?

13 Which band did Freda Payne sing about in 1970?

14 What did the New Seekers want to teach the world to do in 1972?

15 Where did Jimmy Osmond's long-haired lover come from?

●●

ANSWERS

1, A yellow ribbon 2, Waterloo 3, This Christmas 4, Divorce 5, Matchstalks 6, On the Moon 7, Your Rhythm Stick 8, Mississippi 9, The Moon of Love 10, January 11, Your Man 12, Old Dough 13, Band of Gold 14, Sing 15, Liverpool

QUIZ 279
WORLD EVENTS
1978

•••

1 What was historic about the choice of a Pole to be Pope?

2 Which book was no longer China's bestseller?

3 Where was the "Muldergate" scandal?

4 Which Norman entered the shadow cabinet?

5 Where were this year's Nobel Prixes awarded?

6 And to whom?

7 Which country signed a friendship treaty with Afghanistan?

8 The President of Algeria died; who was he?

9 Which European king visited China

10 Where was Mobutu president?

11 What kind of bomb did the USA decide against building?

12 Where was the "Son of Sam" killer sentenced?

13 What nationality was Prince Michael of Kent's bride?

14 Where is Bucharest, visited by Chinese leaders in August?

15 Whom did Prince Charles refuse to talk to at a funeral?

•••

ANSWERS

1, John Paul II was the first non-Italian pope in over 400 years, 2, Mao's *Little Red Book* 3, South Africa 4, Norman St John-Stevas 5, Oslo 6, Menachem Begin and Anwar Sadat 7, The USSR 8, Houari Boumedienne 9, King Juan Carlos of Spain 10, Zaire 11, A neutron bomb 12, New York 13, Austrian 14, Romania 15, Idi Amin (at Jomo Kenyatta's funeral)

QUIZ 280
POT LUCK

1 For which US soccer team did Pele sign in 1975?

2 Which Test cricket team did Clive Lloyd captain?

3 For which FA cup-winning side did Jim Montgomery play in goal?

4 Which prime minister supported Huddersfield Town?

5 Which country owned the Ekofisk oil field?

6 Which horse exercised on Southport beach?

7 Who was King of Jordan?

8 Who starred in the film *Saturday Night Fever*?

9 Where was Bokassa crowned emperor?

10 In which year was Waterloo voted Eurovision Song Contest winner?

11 What was Reginald Perrin's middle name?

12 Who wrote *Not a Penny More, Not a Penny Less*?

13 In the children's TV series, what was the name of Captain Pugwash's pirate ship?

14 Which Nobel Prize did Milton Friedman win?

15 Where was an army of clay soldiers found in a tomb?

ANSWERS

1, New York Cosmos 2, West Indies 3, Sunderland (1973) 4, Harold Wilson 5, Norway 6, Red Rum 7, King Hussein 8, John Travolta 9, Central African Empire 10, 1974 11, Iolanthe 12, Jeffrey Archer 13, The Black Pig 14, Economics 15, China

QUIZ 201
PEOPLE

🐾🐾

1 Which conductor now making music in Berlin made his London debut in 1976?

2 Which is his home city?

3 Who edited *The Times* throughout the 70s?

4 Where did Prince Andrew go to school after Gordonstoun?

5 And which naval college did he then attend?

6 Who wrote a 1978 novel in which Hitler visited Liverpool?

7 With which club did Billy Bonds spend most of his footballing career?

8 Which Welsh actor appeared in *Magic* (1978)?

9 What was the stage name of Francis Alex Howard?

10 Who made an 1971 album called *Ram*?

11 Complete this 1973 show title: *Cowardy* ...?

12 And which Julia was in it?

13 Who wrote the play *Ten Times Table*?

14 Who post-Python was telling *Ripping Yarns*?

15 And what subject was Professor Roger Penrose teaching at Oxford?

🐾🐾

ANSWERS

1, Simon Rattle 2, Liverpool 3, William Rees-Mogg 4, Lakeland College, Ontario 5, Royal Naval College, Dartmouth 6, Beryl Bainbridge 7, West Ham 8, Anthony Hopkins 9, Frankie Howerd 10, Paul McCartney 11, Custard 12, Julia Mackenzie 13, Alan Ayckbourne 14, Michael Palin 15, Mathematics

QUIZ 282
SCIENCE & TECHNOLOGY

1 Where did the Tasaday live?

2 Why did they cause interest in 1971?

3 Where was the then oldet-known human skull in Europe found?

4 What was Cygnus 1?

5 What prehistoric reptile was found near Peterborough?

6 And what kind of house was unearthed in Dover?

7 What was SAS-A?

8 It was also called Uhuru. What does Uhuru mean?

9 Who or what was Washoe?

10 What language did Washoe seem to understand?

11 What was a device called Optacon designed to do?

12 What was unusual about a 200-million-year-old reptile fossil unearthed in 1971?

13 Where was the first heart-and-lung transplant attempted?

14 Why did the Americans crash-land a lunar module on the Moon?

15 Which university had Britain's most powerful computer?

ANSWERS

ARTS & ENTERTAINMENT

1 Who had a hit with *Telegram Sam*?

2 What was singer Nilsson's full name?

3 Which US singer wrote *Vincent*?

4 Who was the 'Vincent' in the title?

5 What year did the song top the UK charts?

6 What other song by the same artist was even better known?

7 Which 9-year-old topped the charts over Christmas 1972?

8 What was Slade's first UK number one (1971)?

9 Who sang *Paper Roses* in 1973?

10 Whose *Merry Xmas Everybody* has stayed in our ears ever since?

11 From which group did Lyn Paul split to go solo?

12 Who sang *Crazy Horses*?

13 Who sang *On Broadway* in 1978?

14 Which TV actor had a hit with *If* in 1975?

15 In which decade was he born?

ANSWERS

POT LUCK

•••

1 Which 70s prime minister married Gladys Mary Baldwin?

2 Which prime minister was born in Grantham, in Lincolnshire?

3 Was Jean Renoir who died in 1979 a painter or a film director?

4 Who wrote books about Inspector Morse?

5 What was Inspector Morse's first name?

6 Who played *Morse* in the successful TV series?

7 In which city was Bertolucci's Last Tango?

8 For which James Bond movie was the largest-ever studio stage built in 1976?

9 Where was it built?

10 Who was the oldest actor ever to win an Oscar (in 1976)?

11 In which film did he star?

12 Who won an Oscar for his role in *Save The Tiger*?

13 Did he play a desperate businessman or a big game hunter?

14 Leonide Massine died in 1979; in which art form had he become famous?

15 Which English team won the Fairs Cup (now the UEFA Cup) in 1972?

•••

ANSWERS

1, Harold Wilson 2, Margaret Thatcher 3, A film director 4, Colin Dexter
5, Endeavour 6, John Thaw 7, Paris 8, *The Spy Who Loved Me* 9, Pinewood Studios
10, George Burns 11, The Sunshine Boys 12, Jack Lemmon
13, A desperate businessman 14, Ballet 15, Tottenham Hotspur

PEOPLE
MARGARET THATCHER

●●●

1 What was Mrs Thatcher's maiden name?

2 What, in 1974, did Mrs Thatcher suggest housewives should do to combat inflation?

3 What was her father's first name?

4 What was the family business?

5 At which university did she study?

6 And what year did she go there?

7 What job did she do after leaving university?

8 What did she study in her spare time?

9 What year did she marry?

10 The names of her children?

11 Which constituency did she win to become an MP?

12 What year did she enter Parliament?

13 What was her only cabinet post before becoming prime minister?

14 What in 1979 did Mrs Thatcher say she was not prepared to settle for a third of?

15 Whom did she beat to get the job?

●●●

ANSWERS

1, Margaret Hilda Roberts 2, Hoard food 3, Alfred 4, A grocery shop 5, Oxford 6, 1943 7, Research chemist 8, Law 9, 1951 10, Mark and Carol 11, Finchley 12, 1959 13, Education Secretary 14, A loaf, referring to her demand for a rebate on Britain's EEC contributions 15, Edward Heath

WORLD EVENTS

1979

●●●

1 In which month did Britain go to the polls?

2 Who said she felt "calm" as she took up office?

3 Which African country had a new "interim" name?

4 Where did President Somoza face a crisis?

5 Where did troops open fire outside a cathedral?

6 Why was the pope going home in June?

7 What was the SALT-2 treaty designed to limit?

8 Which two powers signed it?

9 Which of them was building SS-20s?

10 And what were SS-20s?

11 Which elections were a turn-off for British voters?

12 Which party came out best in the low turnout?

13 Who cut tax by 3p in the pound?

14 Which countries got together in Lusaka?

15 Where was Francisco Nguema deposed?

●●●

ANSWERS

1, May 2, Margaret Thatcher 3, Rhodesia became Zimbabwe-Rhodesia 4, Nicaragua 5, El Salvador 6, He made a visit to his native land, Poland 7, Strategic weapons (missiles) 8, Carter of the USA and Brezhnev of the USSR 9, The USSR 10, Medium-range mobile missiles 11, The 1979 European Parliament elections 12, The Conservatives 13, Britain's new Chancellor of the Exchequer Geoffrey Howe 14, Commonwealth countries 15, Equatorial Guinea

QUIZ 207
POT LUCK

●●●

1 Which British boxer did Muhammad Ali knock out to retain his world title in May 1976?

2 The designer of the giant 'Spruce Goose' died in 1976. Who was this person?

3 What was the 'Goose'?

4 What did George Davis do for a living?

5 Who rode Empery to victory in the 1976 Derby?

6 What was Walter Mondale's nickname?

7 Who became Liberal Party leader in 1976?

8 Whom did he beat?

9 What was Sir Mortimer Wheeler's profession?

10 What was Evonne Goolagong's married name?

11 In which sport did Kornelia Ender win Olympic Gold?

12 What nationality was racing driver Niki Lauda?

13 What was this year's boxing blockbuster at the cinema?

14 Which car's 4 millionth model was made this year?

15 Who played the emperor Claudius, in a TV series?

●●●

ANSWERS

1. Richard Dunn 2. Howard Hughes 3. An aeroplane 4. He was a cab driver 5. Lester Piggott 6. Fritz 7. David Steele 8. John Pardoe 9. An archaeologist 10. Cawley 11. Swimming 12. Austrian 13. Rocky 14. The Mini 15. Derek Jacobi

QUIZ 200
WORLD EVENTS
1979

●●●

1 Which wartime leader was murdered by the IRA in August?

2 What was he doing at the time?

3 In which branch of the services had he served?

4 What relation was the murdered person to the queen?

5 Where did David Dacko overthrow an emperor?

6 Which president found running too much for him?

7 Where was a president shot dead "accidentally"?

8 Which Caribbean islands became independent from British rule?

9 Who said his country was no longer liable for overseas debts?

10 Which newspaper reappeared after a long-running industrial dispute?

11 Where did troops fight for control of Islam's holiest shrine?

12 Who succeeded Jack Lynch as Irish prime minister in December?

13 Who went out to be Rhodesia's last British governor?

14 By what name was the country now to be known?

15 Where in London was the deal ending the Rhodesia crisis signed?

●●●

ANSWERS

1, Lord Mountbatten of Burma 2, He was fishing 3, The Royal Navy 4, He was the queen's uncle 5, Central African Empire 6, President Carter (who almost collapsed while jogging) 7, President Park of South Korea 8, St Vincent and Grenada 9, The Iranian foreign minister 10, The Times 11, Mecca 12, Charles Haughey 13, Christopher Soames (Lord Soames) 14, Zimbabwe 15, Lancaster House

QUIZ 289
POT LUCK

1 With which group did Leslie McKeown sing?

2 Whose real name was Wynette Pugh?

3 *Rivers of Babylon* was a 1978 hit for whom?

4 From which show/film does the song *Summer Nights* come?

5 What name had Alvin Stardust used in the 1960s?

6 What is Sting's original name?

7 How many members had Police?

8 Whose first 11 singles all reached the UK Top Ten?

9 With which 70s group did Ray Dorset appear?

10 Whose Ding-a-Ling topped the charts on both sides of the Atlantic?

11 For which soccer team did Peter Mellor keep goal in a 70s cup final?

12 What other 'month' topped the 70s charts?

13 Who recorded *January*?

14 Who had the other 'month' hit in 1976?

15 Who repeated the Crickets' success with *Oh Boy* in 1975?

ANSWERS

1, The Bay City Rollers 2, Tammy Wynette 3, Boney M 4, *Grease* 5, Shane Fenton 6, Gordon Sumner 7, Three 8, Gary Glitter 9, Mungo Jerry 10, Chuck Berry 11, Fulham (1975) 12, December 63 13, Pilot 14, Four Seasons 15, Mud

QUIZ 290
POT LUCK

●●

1 Where did Babrak Karmal become leader in December 1979?

2 What Nobel Prize did Odysseus Elytis win in 1979?

3 What nationality was he?

4 How high did mortgage rates zoom in November 1979?

5 Whose embassy in Tehran was attacked in 1979?

6 Who beat Billie Jean King in a shock win at Wimbledon?

7 Who set a new mile record in Oslo in July?

8 In which band, formed in 1973, did a guitarist spit fire and fake blood on stage?

9 Which giant planet was found to have rings?

10 Which spacecraft made the discovery?

11 How much was milk per pint in 1979?

12 Who won the 1979 FA Cup Final?

13 Who was Home Secretary in the new Conservative government?

14 Who claimed Jeremy Thorpe had 'seduced' him?

15 In which country was evidence of Khmer Rouge genocide uncovered?

●●

ANSWERS

1, Afghanistan 2, Literature 3, Greek 4, 15 per cent 5, The USA's 6, Tracey Austin 7, Sebastian Coe 8, Kiss 9, Jupiter 10, *Voyager 1* 11, 15p 12, Arsenal 13, William Whitelaw 14, Norman Scott 15, Cambodia

WORLD EVENTS

1979

•••

1 Who denied that Britain was in chaos during the winter?

2 From where had he just returned?

3 Where did the Peacock Throne topple?

4 Who said he would name the government from now on?

5 Which country did China invade to "teach it a lesson"?

6 Where was Abu Hassan blown up?

7 Which 1972 crime had he allegedly planned?

8 Where was US ambassador Adolph Dubs murdered?

9 Who won the Edge Hill by-election for the Liberals?

10 And in which city was the constituency?

11 Which part of the the UK said no to devolution?

12 What kind of accident occurred at Thee Mile Island?

13 Which Tory MP was killed by a car bomb in March?

14 And where did the attack happen?

15 Where did the New Jewel Movement lead a revolution?

•••

ANSWERS

1, Prime minister James Callaghan 2, A summit meeting in Guadeloupe 3, Iran 4, Ayatollah Khomeini 5, Vietnam 6, Beirut 7, The 1972 Munich Olympics massacre 8, Kabul, Afghanistan 9, David Alton 10, Liverpool 11, Wales 12, A nuclear accident 13, Airey Neave 14, The House of Commons car park 15, Grenada

NOTES

NOTES

NOTES

NOTES

NOTES

••

NOTES

NOTES

NOTES

NOTES

NOTES

NOTES

••

NOTES

NOTES

NOTES

NOTES